THE ULTIMATE BASEBALL ACTIVITY BOOK

Crosswords, Word Searches, Puzzles, Fun Facts,
Trivia Challenges and Much More for Baseball Lovers!

KURT TAYLOR

CONTENTS

INTRODUCTION

If you love baseball and you love puzzles and exercising your brain, you'll feel right at home here.

The best baseball players know that the eyes and the brain are the two most critical parts of the body for winning games. This book of baseball-related trivia, puzzles, brain teasers, and other word games will help you train both of these crucial components.

You'll find word searches and scrambles for your eyes, crossword puzzles and memory games for your brainpower and plenty of fun games to simply enjoy with your friends, teammates, family, and other baseball lovers.

There are over 100 puzzles spread across 10 chapters in this book ready for you to solve, and that's not including the trivia, fun facts, and other games along the way.

By the end of this book, you'll know:

- All 30 professional baseball teams and their stadiums.

- Many of the game's greatest players, from past to present.

- Who holds the records for the most hits, home runs, strikeouts, etc.

- How to play many fun and exciting baseball games.

- Quirky stories and baseball oddities that even the most die-hard fans don't know.

- How to properly spell names like Saltalamacchia and Yastrzemski.

- Fun baseball facts to surprise your friends.

- Many of the unsung heroes of the Negro Leagues.

- And much more!

Thanks to this baseball puzzle book for adults, you'll have hours of fun. It's the perfect companion for a long road trip or while you watch your favorite baseball team on TV. If you're a player or coach, take the book to practice and quiz the whole team.

Some puzzles are harder to solve than others. If you get stuck or aren't sure about an answer, check the back of the puzzle book for solutions.

Enjoy!

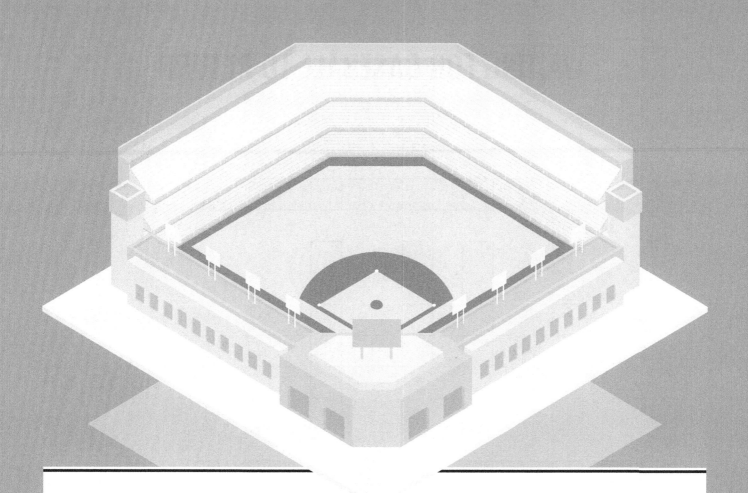

CHAPTER

1

SPRING TRAINING

It's time to dust off the rust from the offseason and get back to work. Spring Training is a time when fans and players get a little taste of the sport they love so much. Prospects rub shoulders with veterans and try to show coaches, the team, fans, and themselves what they can do at the highest level of play.

The puzzles in this section aim to encapsulate the feeling of Spring Training and the buildup as the baseball world edges closer to Opening Day.

WAITING FOR BASEBALL TO RETURN

WAITING FOR BASEBALL TO RETURN

Across

2. The spring home to both the Red Sox and the Twins.

6. Spring Training attendee who isn't on the 40-man roster.

9. A sour citrus and a Spring Training league.

13. The only fielder facing the other direction.

15. A near-religious event in Boston. Everywhere else, it's a day when equipment trucks head down to Spring Training facilities.

16. A prickly plant and a Spring Training league.

17. Original Winter Meetings location.

19. "I've tried a lot of things in the off-season, but the only thing I really know is baseball." - Hank _____

20. "The saddest day of the year is the day baseball seasons ends." Tommy _____

22. A Spring Training double-header.

23. Happens on the last day of the Winter Meetings.

Down

1. Another name for baseball's offseason, particularly free-agent signings and Winter Meetings.

3. Home to the Diamondbacks during the regular season and the Brewers in spring.

4. The NY Yankees take over this Florida team's hometown during Spring Training.

5. The day in March that is (usually) the first day of spring.

7. The spring home to both the Padres and Mariners.

8. Reports to Spring Training at the same time as #13 Across.

10. "The Rajah" who stares out the window and waits for spring.

11. "Spring Training is a time to think about being young again." - Ernie _____

12. "It's the fans that need Spring Training." - Harry _____

14. An older player people look to for advice.

18. A game between teammates.

21. Designated for assignment abbreviation.

A NEW SEASON

```
P V J E C Q W S R G R Q C R V V F
Q S H N Q L P B P X O S F E P Q B
E F C V W R I O V F J M Q D T Z X
X D K H I Y S N S J Y R K E L R Q
P X A N E R U P E C Z E P M Y R V
E P G U V D U K L U P W Q P A M E
C Q K X T T U M Y A P H C T A R T
T M A H G P G L H P Y Y R I G O A
A J K B O Y E A E Z F B Z O A O L
T S K R O W E R I F V F A N A K S
I P O P N O E R K X O U P L F I N
O O X N N E W P L A Y E R S L E A
N M A E T E T I R O V A F P U S E
S T A K V A N F I T G L T O Y O L
O K S E C A F R A I L I M A F B C
R M N T Y S O F Y B E Y A O V X Z
X N Q A J T M Q C C G Q S M U O T
```

Clean Slate	New Players
Expectations	Play Ball
Familiar Faces	Redemption
Favorite Team	Rookies
Fireworks	Schedule
Lineup	Spring

THE FUNDAMENTALS

```
X G F B V U N P Q H U W S S F L R Z H O O O T K
B E P R H N I N R H E U B U S V C A S O V L H G
K E Q E P M Q T U A R Q A I I P V T F R F U C R
U S I D B O X Z G R C V T P Y V A L X E H E V A
J X S N E Y P J S E E T I E O A H T S M Y T A N
Y O M U V V S F W K G M I B V T L Y Q Q X M Y D
T O O O M B O Y L X E C O C J M S P B H X A C S
K B H R K Y B L W Y K S Y H E J P T E B M E B L
F Y A G O V D E G N A R E T E V F C R L I N U A
S R B L I Q N B I N P P E N H D T J Q O B N M M
O K A B L D S Y Q S U H Q V R J M E I Z H U I L
O C S A Z S J B F G W J Y R E G A N A M P S O I
U A E T S Q Q T U O E K I R T S Q P C K W S U D
T L R T X R E I K O O R B H L U N F I L C P T Q
F B U I W R H B Z Z C A B U N T I N G J K G S F
I E N N O Y A J O A S N N Z Z E S G O Q V C V P
E Y N G K T W F T E T E U K L T N D Z R Z G K J
L E I P D K Y C B R C Y Y D T L E B I L W W J P
D I N H U Y H A A M X V I I R E H C T I P Y G R
F C G X D E L I N X L N M Z M X S G W D D C Y R
A U T Y L N R Y O G Q M L R T C H K H C A O C
N I R G U H L K R I I D L E I F N I D E E O L
S F N G N Y A G V X Z F W T Q C Y B C W F T W O
X V I G K Z I S Z Q L B H Q D R I L L S A X E V
```

Drills	Baserunning	Coach	Infield	Practice
Fans	Bunting	Double Play	Manager	Rookie
Eye Black	Balls	Fielding	Outfield	Shortstop
Mitt	Baseball	Grand Slam	Outs	Strikeout
Glove	Batting	Grounder	Pitcher	Training
Bat	Catcher	Home Run	Pop Fly	Veteran

BACK TO BASICS

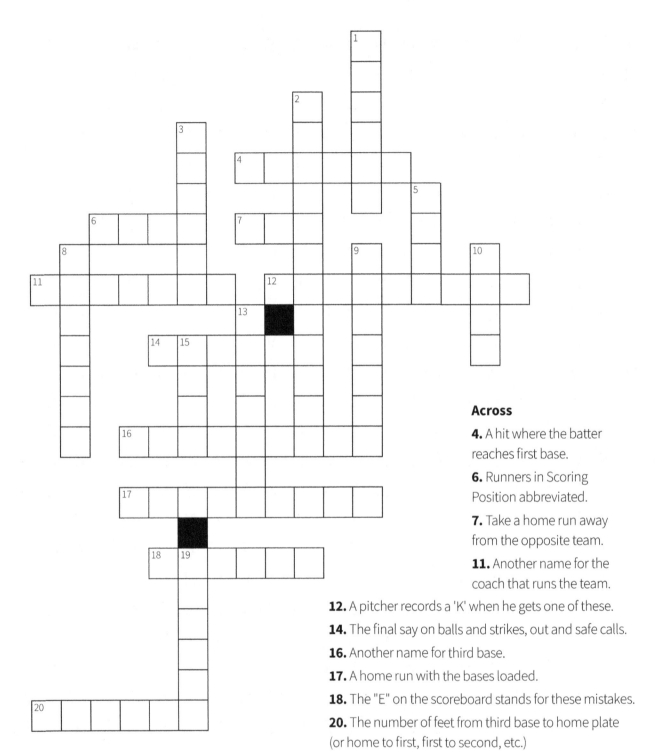

Across

4. A hit where the batter reaches first base.

6. Runners in Scoring Position abbreviated.

7. Take a home run away from the opposite team.

11. Another name for the coach that runs the team.

12. A pitcher records a 'K' when he gets one of these.

14. The final say on balls and strikes, out and safe calls.

16. Another name for third base.

17. A home run with the bases loaded.

18. The "E" on the scoreboard stands for these mistakes.

20. The number of feet from third base to home plate (or home to first, first to second, etc.)

Down

1. A hit where the batter reaches second base.

2. RBI meaning.

3. A hit where the batter reaches third base.

5. Number of defensive players on the field at once.

8. The player behind the dish.

9. Hurler, Ace, #1 position.

10. Need three of these to get out of an inning.

13. The shape of the field.

15. What a catcher wears on his hand.

19. A new technology in baseball used for close plays.

MATCH THE TEAMS TO THE SPRING TRAINING LEAGUES

Chicago Cubs

Washington Nationals

Houston Astros

Miami Marlins

New York Yankees

Texas Rangers

San Diego Padres

Pittsburgh Pirates

Colorado Rockies

Seattle Mariners

Toronto Blue Jays

Kansas City Royals

Baltimore Orioles

Oakland Athletics

Arizona Diamondbacks

Boston Red Sox

Tampa Bay Rays

Atlanta Braves

Los Angeles Dodgers

Milwaukee Brewers

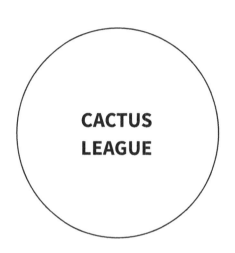

SPRING TRAINING STADIUM UNSCRAMBLE

1. OGEGER M ERRSEBITNNNE DEFLI _____

2. BUEELTJ KARP _____

3. CEROLV PRAK _____

4. ETCLORAHT SRPOST RAKP _____

5. TD ARLLKBPA _____

6. OGRER ANDE THECEOVLR TUSAIDM _____

7. ARGOYOED RKAALPLB _____

8. OREPIA PSORTS LOPXCME _____

9. SESDCTTLOA ITSDAUM _____

10. LNASO RAPK _____

11. MTEEP IBLDOA TUASIDM _____

12. MADMHON DAMTISU _____

13. ED SMTHI ITUMSDA _____

14. AMCEACBKL RCANH NGEALEDL _____

FUN FACT: *Hall of Fame Centerfielder Tris Speaker didn't get off to a strong career start. He played for only seven games with the Red Sox, hitting .158, before being released. Unable to find any other interested parties, he paid his own way to the Red Sox training camp in Little Rock, Arkansas. The Red Sox then turned Speaker's contract over to the Little Rock Travelers as payment for renting their field.*

Luckily for Speaker, the Red Sox held the right to buy his contract back for $500, which they did less than a year later. He would go on to help the Red Sox to multiple World Series titles.

GRAPEFRUIT LEAGUE TEAM LOCATIONS MAP

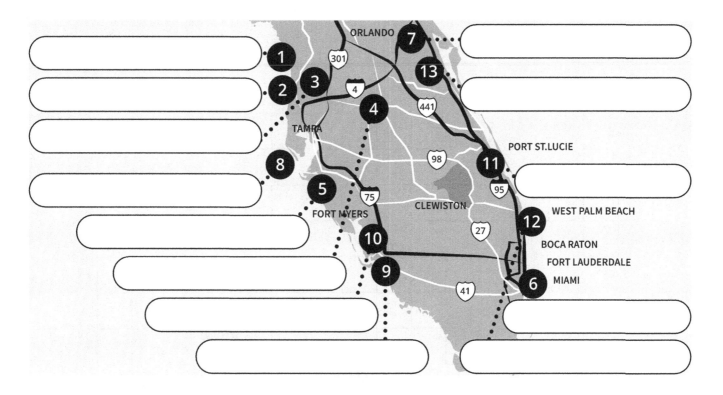

CACTUS LEAGUE TEAM LOCATIONS MAP

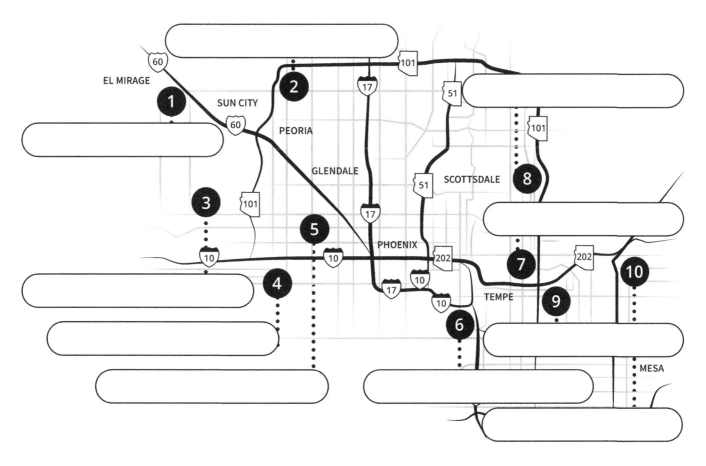

BASEBALL SLANG

BASEBALL SLANG

Across

3. "Dingers," "Tater," "Four-bagger", and "Leaving the yard" all mean one of these.

5. You want to break this out when there's a long home run.

7. A home run that is long and high, almost reaching a celestial object.

8. Another name for the Major Leagues and a baseball video game franchise.

13. Another name for home plate and something you eat off of.

15. Hitting a single, double, triple, and home run in the same game.

17. A hard hit ball back to the pitcher.

18. A pitcher may be throwing this three-letter word if he's pitching with high velocity.

19. Another name for a no-hitter.

20. Throwing the ball around the bases is also known as throwing it around this.

21. A "worm burner" is a comical name for this type of hit in the dirt.

22. Free baseball happens when the game goes into these.

Down

1. A very good pitcher, usually a team's number one starter.

2. Something you don't want to touch in the kitchen and baseball's offseason rumor mill.

4. Another name for a base.

6. The alleys or gaps are the spots between these players.

9. These are on the pond when you have multiple runners on base.

10. Another name for the pitcher's mound and TV dad Hank's last name.

11. A player is a threat to steal a base if he's got a good set of these.

12. You're caught doing this if you let the third strike go by without swinging.

14. Another name for a pitcher.

16. You might find this in your kitchen cabinets. It's also an easy pop fly.

WHO SAID IT? SPRING TRAINING EDITION

1. "I love playing this game and every Spring Training feels like the first."

A. Rickey Henderson

2. "People who write about Spring Training not being necessary have never tried to throw a baseball."

B. Harry Caray

3. "Fighting for a job — that's been my mindset every Spring Training."

C. Jim Palmer

4. "It's the fans that need Spring Training. You gotta get 'em interested. Wake 'em up and let 'em know that their season is coming, the good times are gonna roll."

D. Curt Schilling

5. "Spring Training was always a combination of relaxing and working, and I missed that quite a bit. I missed being around the ball field. A baseball, a bat, the smell of the uniform, you might say. Talking baseball. Seeing opponents as well as the Cubs."

E. Sandy Koufax

6. "I hate the cursed Oriole fundamentals. I've been doing them since 1964. I do them in my sleep. I hate Spring Training."

F. Aaron Judge

7. "A young ballplayer looks on his first Spring Training trip as a stage-struck young woman regards the theater."

G. Christy Mathewson

8. "Before I pitch any game, from Spring Training to Game 7 of the World Series, I'm scared to death."

H. Lou Boudreau

FUN FACT: *Spring Training is almost as old as baseball itself. In 1870, the Cincinnati Red Stockings and Chicago White Stockings held baseball camps in New Orleans. Years later, the Washington Capitals of the National League organized a four-day camp in Jacksonville, FL. By the turn of the century, Spring Training was a staple.*

Unknown communities in Arizona and Florida (Tucson, Fort Lauderdale, Sarasota, etc.) suddenly became popular destinations because of baseball's impact.

PLAYER POSITIONS IN NUMBERS

1. Shortstop

2. Pitcher

3. Center Fielder

4. Left Fielder

5. First Baseman

6. Catcher

7. Right Fielder

8. Third Baseman

9. Second Baseman

A. Position #3

B. Position #5

C. Position #7

D. Position #1

E. Position #8

F. Position #2

G. Position #4

H. Position #6

I. Position #9

BASEBALL MATHEMATICS

Using the position numbers above, see if you can understand the following equation.

$$4 \quad + \quad 6 \quad + \quad 3 \quad = \quad 2$$

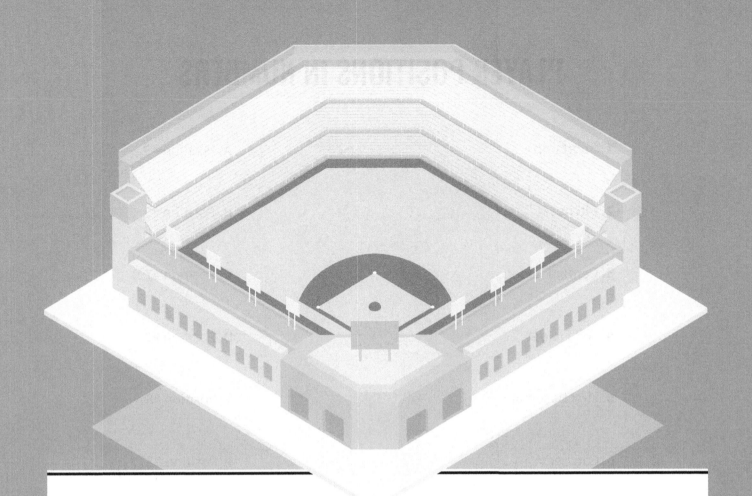

CHAPTER
2
OPENING DAY

Opening day is a clean slate for every team. With 162 games to play, everything is plausible. Records may be broken, history made, and legends born. Yet, none of this can happen before Opening Day starts. Finally, baseball is back!

The puzzles, trivia, and games in this section capture the excitement Opening Day brings to baseball.

BEST OPENING DAY MOMENTS

Across

3. After a tragic plane crash killed Roberto Clemente the season before, the Pirates started 1973 by retiring his uniform number.

6. This Hall of Famer returned to the Mariners in 2001 and promptly hit his 8th career Opening Day home run, tying the record.

8. This team won its inaugural game against the Dodgers and officially brought baseball to the Sunshine State.

9. The old Yankee Stadium was known as "The House That ____ Built." The player in question christened the opener of the park in 1923 with a home run.

11. Opening Day in 1995 brought back baseball after this occurred the season before.

12. Cubs' Karl "Tuffy" Rhodes was an unlikely hero in 1994's Opening Day. Not known for power (only 13 career home runs), he clubbed three dingers off this Mets Cy Young winner.

14. This legendary pitcher threw a 13-inning shutout against the Athletics in 1919.

15. Pedro Ramos shut out a tough Yankees lineup on the road and gave this team its first win in history.

16. The 1901 Tigers scored this many runs in the bottom of the ninth inning and set the greatest Opening Day comeback in history.

17. With the first swing of this player's 1974 season, he tied Babe Ruth's record of 714 career home runs.

Down

1. Opening Day at Fenway Park in 1973 saw the first plate appearance by this offense-focused position.

2. In 1940, this Cleveland pitcher threw the first and only no-hitter to occur on Opening Day.

4. This player set the record for Opening Day home runs in 1975 and also became the first African-American manager in baseball history.

5. Any Opening Day featuring a rivalry matchup between the Cubs and Cardinals is sure to stand out. The 1971 contest was a particularly good one, ending in a walk-off home run in the 10th by Billy Williams off this Cardinals HOF pitcher.

7. Opening Day in 1947 changed the world when this player took the field and broke the color barrier.

10. This future Yankees captain made a big splash with a home run on Opening Day of his 1996 rookie year.

13. This US President (last name) started an Opening Day tradition by throwing out the first pitch of the game.

FIRST DAY JITTERS

Caught Leaning

Missed the Sign

Errant Throw

Interference

Dropped Pop Fly

Mishandled

Grounder

Caught Looking

Picked Off

Sun in the Eyes

Caught in a Pickle

Through the Legs

Error

Mental Error

Passed Ball

Missed Cutoff Man

Wild Pitch

Blooper

Bobble

```
O X L G N I K O O L T H G U A C K B I X C P W J
A A H F F L J E O G P Q X Z Z O C G S J A R M U
O I L Y D J V W G Q I J C S C E T G F L J I U O
I T T C M M Z P A R Y X F P U J E Z T S S B K D
M N D Y Q E E I A R O S Q C Q L B R O S Q E L C
I S M P M B F N S S G T A L E C T C E P D J D Y
S C U X E L Q S T M S U B H R X O D Z Q Q R F S
H O Z N G R M W U A G E T X M R T U D H O N W M
A L C A I F R S I H L H D D D H Q I H P G P C I
N T A S E N I A T L G E V B E N K R P H I Z Q S
D Q U W X G T L N U D M R S A K O E P C U H Y S
L V G X A V E H O T F P I R U L D F K L A K M E
E F H R I A U R E P T G I E O P L E G S R W C D
D E T S N K H R T E N H U T O R D U H B U N Q C
G P I I J T A N S T Y V R P C O A S F O E C J U
R Q N F Q M H B S J L E F O F H Y U Z R D Q R T
O G A G M C Y L L D J L S F W Z M E E L N Q E O
U O P L P O Z O Q D Y V R U Q Z R F R Z A T K F
N I I M Q O P O F A F V H F T X R O Y W U E D F
D P C D Q H Q P X X P Q Q P V E P X J S C Z Z M
E P K R D Q I E R Y B Q J X T K B C Q K A Z M A
R T L U B Z R R N T E W R N E L B B O B J U K N
Q R E E F O G K C N W L I I S A T P X N N G N M
V P K E R R O R Q B G U O A W I B X M X A X K B
```

WORLD SERIES REMATCH

Match the World Series winners on the left with the teams they faced on the right.

2021 Atlanta Braves	Philadelphia Phillies
2015 Kansas City Royals	St. Louis Browns
2009 New York Yankees	New York Yankees
2004 Boston Red Sox	Baltimore Orioles
2001 Arizona Diamondbacks	Chicago Cubs
1997 Florida Marlins	Houston Astros
1996 New York Yankees	Atlanta Braves
1990 Cincinnati Reds	Pittsburgh Pirates
1984 Detroit Tigers	New York Mets
1979 Pittsburgh Pirates	Milwaukee Braves
1974 Oakland Athletics	Boston Braves
1965 Los Angeles Dodgers	Minnesota Twins
1958 New York Yankees	St. Louis Cardinals
1953 New York Yankees	San Diego Padres
1948 Cleveland Indians	New York Giants
1945 Detroit Tigers	Oakland Athletics
1944 St. Louis Cardinals	Washington Senators
1936 New York Yankees	Los Angeles Dodgers
1933 New York Giants	Cleveland Indians
1903 Boston Americans	Brooklyn Dodgers

OPENING DAY ABROAD

Across

3. Opening Day went 'Down Under' in 2014 when a field for this sport was converted to a baseball diamond in Sydney, Australia.

4. This California team has participated in the most Opening Day games abroad.

6. This stadium in Japan has been the home for the most international Opening Day games.

7. The first Opening Day game abroad was in 1999 between the Rockies and Padres in this country.

8. This team lost both games played in Sydney, Australia against the Los Angeles Dodgers.

Down

1. In 2004, the Tampa Bay Devil Rays split a two-game opening series with this New York team in Japan.

2. The 2019 Opening Day festivities in Tokyo saw the end of this Japan-born MLB player's career.

5. An Opening Day game played on this Caribbean Island in 2001 saw the Rangers lose to the Blue Jays 8-1.

WHO SAID IT? OPENING DAY EDITION

1. "You always get a special kick on opening day, no matter how many you go through. You look forward to it like a birthday party when you're a kid. You think something wonderful is going to happen."

A. Joe DiMaggio

2. "There's nothing like Opening Day. There's nothing like the start of a new season."

B. Mary Schmich

3. "In baseball, no other day is so pure with possibility. No scores yet, no losses, no blame or disappointment. No hangover, at least until the game's over."

C. Rob Sheffield

4. "There is no sports event like Opening Day of baseball."

D. George Brett

5. "Baseball's Opening Day is full of time-honored traditions: the President throws out the first ball, the Cubs' starting pitcher walks away with a 54.00 ERA, the Royals get mathematically eliminated from the pennant race."

E. Pete Rose

6. "It's like Christmas, except it's warmer."

F. George Vecsey

7. "An Opener is not like any other game. There's that little extra excitement, a faster beating of the heart. You know that when you win the first one, you can't lose them all."

G. Jimmy Rollins

8. "The good thing about Opening Day, at the end of the day, it counts. It's in the record."

H. Early Wynn

FUN FACT: *Boston Braves fans attending Opening Day in 1946 stormed to the front office by the hundreds. The problem? A fresh coat of red paint on the outfield stands hadn't dried yet. There were lots of paint-stained clothes that day. The Braves agreed to pay for the spectators' cleaning bills and avoided an Opening Day riot.*

FAMOUS IN THE BOOTH

1. IHLACME KYA _____

2. YREJR ANLOMEC _____

3. NOJ LMREIL _____

4. ERRYJ RMEY _____

5. OJE OMRAGN _____

6. OJHN LRGTNESI _____

7. CKJA UKBC _____

8. EML ALELN _____

9. RSUS EDGSOH _____

10. OBB SOTSAC _____

11. RYAHR ASKAL _____

12. CIKD BRNEGE _____

13. TMI ARMECVCR _____

14. EADV SNAEHIU _____

15. RNEIE HLLAREW _____

16. RYRHA RAACY _____

17. HPLI OTUZIRZ _____

18. DRE RBBERA _____

19. BOB ECEKRU _____

20. IVN YLUCSL _____

FUN FACT: _Ernie Harwell is one of the most legendary announcers and broadcasters in the history of baseball. He was so good, in fact, that Dodgers executive Branch Rickey arranged a trade for Harwell involving one of his own players. Catcher Cliff Dapper went to the Atlanta Crackers and Ernie Harwell became an announcer for the Dodgers. Harwell would ultimately go to the New York Giants and be replaced in Brooklyn by a young man recently graduated from Fordham University named Vin Scully._

OPENING DAY SECRET CRYPTOGRAM

A	B	C	D	E	F	G	H	I	J	K	L	M	N	O	P	Q	R	S	T	U	V	W	X	Y	Z
B										A	C								Z						

```
 T  A  K                    T        T           T              A  L  L           A
 Z  B  A  X     U  X     D  Y  Z     Z  D     Z  P  X     W  B  C  C        E  B  U  X

 T  A  K                 T        T        T
 Z  B  A  X     U  X     D  Y  Z     U  K  Z  P     Z  P  X        Q  L  D  V  I

                                        A        T              A
 W  Y  O     D  X     R  D  D  X     F  X  B  M  Y  Z  R     B  M  I

           A     K              A     K
 Q  L  B  Q  A  X  L     H  B  Q  A

          T        A                             T
 K     I  D  M     Z     Q  B  L  X     K  J     K     M  X  T  X  L     E  X  Z

          A     K
 W  B  Q  A

 L     T              T              T
 C  X  Z     U  X     L  D  D  Z     L  D  D  Z     L  D  D  Z     J  D  L

       T                    T     A
 Z  P  X     P  D  U  X     Z  X  B  U

          T              T                 T           A
 K  J     Z  P  X  O     I  D  M     Z     V  K  M     K  Z     R     B

             A
 R  P  B  U  X

          T              T                 T
 J  D  L     K  Z     R     D  M  Z     Z  V  D     Z  P  L  X  X

                      T                       T
 R  Z  L  K  A  X  R     Z  P  X  O     O  D  Y     L  X     D  I  Z

    A  T        T              L           A  L  L              T
    B  Z     Z  P  X     D  C  I     W  B  C  C     E  B  U  X
```

ERNIE HARWELL OPENING DAY POEM

Ernie Harwell perfectly encapsulated baseball and the feeling of Opening Day. Fill in the blanks of the poem using the word bank below.

Baseball is the _____ tossing out the first ball of the season and a scrubby schoolboy

playing catch with his dad on a Mississippi farm. A tall, thin, old man waving a _____

from the corner of his dugout. That's baseball.

And so is the big fat guy with a bulbous nose running home one of his 714 home runs. There's a man

in Mobile who remembers that Honus _____ hit a triple in Pittsburgh forty-six-years-ago.

That's baseball. So is the scout reporting that a sixteen-year-old _____ pitcher in Cheyenne is

a coming Walter Johnson.

Baseball is a spirited race of man against man, reflex against reflex. A game of _____ .

Every skill is measured, every heroic, every failing is seen and cheered, or booed, and then becomes

a _____ . In Baseball _____ shines its clearest. The only race that matters

is the race to the bag. The creed is a rulebook and color merely something to distinguish one team's

_____ from another.

Baseball is a _____ , his experience no bigger than the lump in his throat as he begins

fulfillment of his dream. It's a veteran too, a tired old man of thirty-five hoping that those aching

_____ can pull him through a sweltering August and September.

ERNIE HARWELL OPENING DAY POEM

Baseball is the cool, clear eyes of Rogers Hornsby, the flashing spikes of _____ Baseball,

it's just a game, as simple as a ball and _____ , and yet as complex as the American

spirit it symbolizes. It's a sport, a business, sometimes almost even _____ .

Why the faerie tale of Willie Mays dashing off to play _____ in the streets with his teenage

pals. That's baseball. And so is the husky voice of a doomed Lou Gehrig saying, "I consider myself the

_____ man on the face of this earth."

Baseball is cigar smoke, hot roasted _____ , ladies' day, "down in front," Take me out to

the Ballgame and The Star-Spangled Banner.

_____ telling the nation's business leaders, 'You have to be a man to be a Big Leaguer, but

you have to have a lot of little _____ in you, too.'

This is a game for America. Still a game of America.

WORD BANK

RELIGION	MUSCLES	PRESIDENT	UNIFORM
CAMPANELLA	STICKBALL	PEANUTS	
WAGNER	TY COBB	BOY	BAT
LUCKIEST	DEMOCRACY	SCORECARD	
STATISTIC	SANDLOT	ROOKIE	INCHES

PRESIDENTIAL FIRST PITCHES

Across

2. Presidents used to toss out the first pitch from the stands. Who was the first to do it from the mound?

3. The other president (aside from Carter) to never throw out a first pitch while in office.

5. After being introduced as a rookie from Arkansas, this president threw the first pitch from the mound to reach the catcher without a bounce.

6. Because it was customary for presidents to throw from the stands rather than the mound, these "first pitches" were initially called this.

9. Washington D.C. has been home to the most presidential first pitches. However, this nearby city became the setting for first pitches from multiple presidents when D.C. was without its own team.

12. Harry S. Truman was the first president to use this hand to make his pitch.

13. Anaheim in 1973 witnessed the first presidential first pitch to take place outside of D.C. Who tossed the pitch?

Down

1. The first pitch tradition took a four-year hiatus during World War II. This president brought the honor back in 1946.

4. Next to Opening Day, this event during the baseball season has seen the most presidential first pitches.

7. This president started the tradition of throwing out the first pitch.

8. The number of different cities President George W. Bush tossed out an Opening Day first pitch in.

10. Jimmy Carter never threw out a presidential first pitch. Including Carter, how many presidents have avoided the tradition?

11. Barack Obama received a mix of boos and laughs when he put on a hat of his favorite Chicago baseball team prior to throwing the first pitch at the Nationals home opener in 2010.

PLAYER-MANAGERS

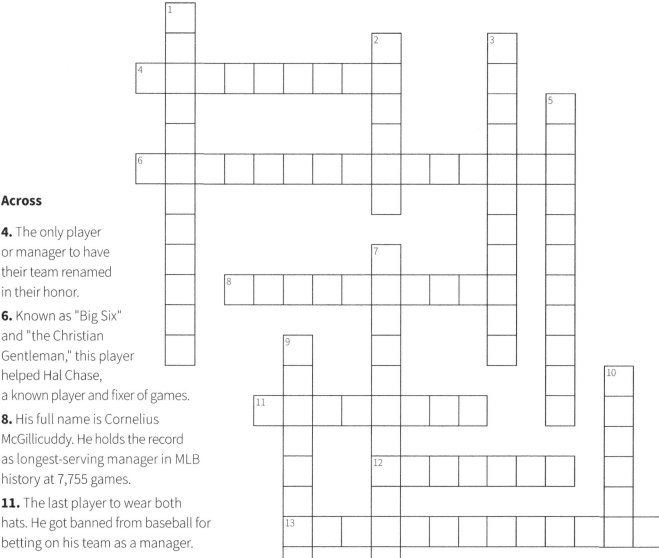

Across

4. The only player or manager to have their team renamed in their honor.

6. Known as "Big Six" and "the Christian Gentleman," this player helped Hal Chase, a known player and fixer of games.

8. His full name is Cornelius McGillicuddy. He holds the record as longest-serving manager in MLB history at 7,755 games.

11. The last player to wear both hats. He got banned from baseball for betting on his team as a manager.

12. The award named in his honor is coveted by pitchers. It's easy to forget he managed the Boston Americans in 1907, too.

13. This player was an off-and-on player-manager for several different teams. His nickname is "The Rajah."

Down

1. Known best for signing Jackie Robinson to the Brooklyn Dodgers, this individual once spent a season as a player, manager, and executive of the St. Louis Browns.

2. He is one of only six players to play 20+ years with the same team. Six of those years he played right field and managed the New York Giants.

3. A player-manager for Cleveland. His team won the World Series against Brooklyn in 1920 while he was manager and outfielder.

5. "The Flying Dutchman" played his final season as player and manager of the Pittsburgh Pirates.

7. A fierce player and fiery manager. He managed Jackie Robinson for part of the 1947 season but was suspended.

9. He only served 18 days as a player-manager for the New York Mets. However, he's much better known as the manager of the other New York team from 1996 to 2007.

10. "The Georgia Peach" took on double duty as fielder and manager for the Detroit Tigers spanning from 1921 to 1926.

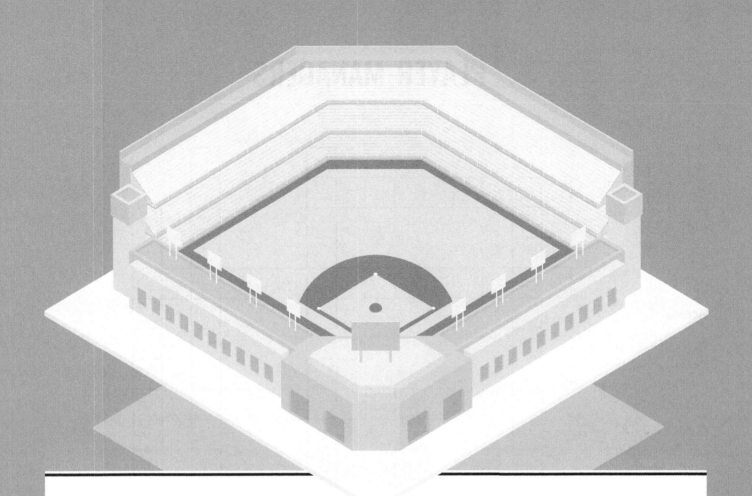

CHAPTER

3

BALLPARKS AND TEAMS

Every baseball fan has their favorite team, and nothing quite compares to seeing a game at their home stadium. The sounds, sights, smells, and, of course, the tastes culminate to create the perfect ballpark experience.

Grab your favorite stadium food and prepare for more puzzles and games. It's all about teams, ballparks, peanuts, and Crackerjacks in this chapter.

TEAM UNSCRAMBLE

1. LOS NELASGE DDESORG

_____

2. PAMAT BAY SRYA

_____

3. LROOCDOA KCREOIS

_____

4. WUEKMIEAL EESRWBR

_____

5. HTOIWGSNNA IANOTNSAL

_____

6. ASTINENOM WTISN

_____

7. ARZONIA ANOMDCIKADBS

_____

8. TORTNOO BELU JYAS

_____

9. BLAORMITE IEOLOSR

_____

10. ENW KRYO SEMT

_____

11. MAMII SIARNML

_____

12. ETTESAL IMARSERN

_____

13. IGCACOH SCBU

_____

14. ANS IOGED ADPRES

_____

15. ASEXT NRAERGS

_____

16. OREMAITBL OROESLI

_____

TEAMS & STADIUMS

1. Tampa Bay Rays

2. Colorado Rockies

3. Pittsburgh Pirates

4. American Family Field

5. Yankee Stadium

6. Petco Park

7. Oakland Athletics

8. Progressive Field

9. Seattle Mariners

10. Toronto Blue Jays

11. Camden Yards

12. Nationals Park

13. Houston Astros

14. Kauffman Stadium

15. Cincinnati Reds

16. Guaranteed Rate Field

17. Miami Marlins

18. Boston Red Sox

19. Dodger Stadium

20. Comerica Park

21. Chase Field

22. New York Mets

23. Busch Stadium

24. Angel Stadium

25. Citizens Bank Park

26. Wrigley Field

A. Los Angeles Angels

B. Los Angeles Dodgers

C. Citi Field

D. Arizona Diamondbacks

E. Cleveland Guardians

F. Coors Field

G. LoanDepot Park

H. San Diego Padres

I. Great American Ball Park

J. Chicago White Sox

K. Detroit Tigers

L. PNC Park

M. Washington Nationals

N. Philadelphia Phillies

O. Kansas City Royals

P. St. Louis Cardinals

Q. Tropicana Field

R. T-Mobile Park

S. Fenway Park

T. Milwaukee Brewers

U. New York Yankees

V. Rogers Centre

W. Chicago Cubs

X. RingCentral Coliseum

Y. Minute Maid Park

Z. Baltimore Orioles

MLB TEAMS

```
H D J X V U E H N J U R U M A Z J T H V M T C P
A K I M Q A A Z Z E P R A O B S O R T S A I Y H
V M U B I C J Q L T A R R R S R E G D O D P Q F
W W H L V M A Y F N I E O O O D B O G B L L F J
L W A B E O Y P G N D C J Y S B M O R I O L E S
W J W T W T V E E S K Z A E X O S E T I H W R S
K J S Y V B R R O I G L V R N Q E N I I I E Q V
U S J C G S S X E Y S A S W K N B D D A S K D Y
R C V O G P D S P S R K X S R A K O Z W A Z W B
Q P I R A T E S H B Y A P N F T K Q J F C H U B
G S L E G N A D I P T A O G O I T O T Q N M X Y
S T Q R I A A T L R X P J D N O B I R G M B A V
U Q B C V R G Q L M S T B E T N K S G W U N Q S
E F K F O N U B I R K Y R N U A G B C E K E B K
E V C U Y X A V E E J C A T G L C A V E R N X C
K S C J U H R S S V A E M R Q S B Z E V O S N A
M Z H I S J D J C R K E B O T S M S L M A I U B
A B D Y C T I G D I N A U R O N S T U H B W H D
R V V U A Z A I I Y T D L C E S S W S R C T R N
L I B L D W N W U A O E F W J W D D A P W A R O
I S O Z Y A S A R P N K L G Y H E B H I R U K M
N L K R L D C A Y R G T A H N M R R N J Q W A A
S L L S W Z R D R V H C S Y T G R S S J W J U I
P A D R E S J O E O H T J C A A Y C Q S H B R D
```

Giants	Athletics	Royals	Nationals	Rays
Rockies	Astros	Tigers	Mets	Reds
Diamondbacks	Mariners	White Sox	Orioles	Pirates
Padres	Rangers	Braves	Yankees	Cubs
Dodgers	Twins	Phillies	Red Sox	Cardinals
Angels	Guardians	Marlins	Blue Jays	Brewers

BALLPARKS ACROSS AMERICA

```
Z D L E I F E T A R D E E T N A R A U G Z K K I
P O C E C N I K A U F F M A N S T A D I U M R J
D R N W H K Z F Y T R U I S T P A R K F J Y A O
A I B N A R S E B W B K R A P O C T E P X R P L
M O U D S A F N J M G W P F Y A Z K J E D T K V
E L Y L E P M W M U I D A T S R E G D O D A N M
R E G E F L U A M D G N T I Z J S J Q F Q R A O
I P I I L E Y U K M L U M P S K M S F Z G B E E
C A R F E A S P I U R U O T O B D N F E I E S W
A R O E L B I A D O X A I B E B I M H Y P T N E
N K G V D N L R A D R W P D E M I V B W Q F E O
F A E I O A O K T L C A C T A L A L U F Z I Z U
A T R S M C C M S E C I C P O T I I E Q W E I K
M C S S J I L P L I O P S L N P S F D P G L T L
I A C E V R A D E F M C D T E C E H E P A D I B
L M E R O E R L G A E Y J J T P P D C F A R C P
Y D N G H M T E N N R P L P Z E A A N S I R K R
F E T O T A N I A A I W F V G F O R R A U E K Z
I N R R R T E F O C C Y E A K B O Z K K O B L D
E Y E P X A C I Q I A S H G A Y K F Y Q E L U D
L A S U P E G T O P P O C O O R S F I E L D W W
D R A C P R N I K O A M U I D A T S E E K N A Y
I D O O K G I C R R R K R A P S L A N O I T A N
Q S I X W L R P G T K C D L E I F Y E L G I R W
```

Yankee Stadium
Wrigley Field
Truist Park
Tropicana Field
Target Field
T Mobile Park
Rogers Centre
RingCentral Coliseum

Progressive Field
PNC Park
Petco Park
Oriole Park at Camden Yards
Oracle Park
Nationals Park
Minute Maid Park
LoanDepot Park

Kauffman Stadium
Guaranteed Rate Field
Great American Ball Park
Globe Life Field
Dodger Stadium
Coors Field
Fenway Park

Comerica Park
Citizens Bank Park
Citi Field
Chase Field
Busch Stadium
Angel Stadium
American Family Field

THE WACKY AND WEIRD MINOR LEAGUES

Across

3. A favorite bath time accessory of Sesame Street's Ernie (plural), and a Minor League Baseball team in Akron, OH.

6. *Game of Thrones* fans kept waiting for these to show up. Instead, they could have caught a Minor League Baseball game in Dayton, OH.

9. It's a bird, it's a plane, it's the Flying Squirrels! Which state capital city is home to this team?

10. A beer ingredient, the name of Hillsboro, OR's baseball team, and what a basketball player needs to dunk.

11. In *The Simpsons*, the local baseball team is the Isotopes. This is also a real Minor League Baseball team from this New Mexico city.

12. Combine another word for waste or garbage with China's iconic black and white bears and you get the Minor League team of Rocket City, AL.

Down

1. Tim Tebow's baseball career saw him playing in Binghamton for this Minor League Baseball team.

2. An oxymoron, delicious seafood dish, and the Marlins Triple-A affiliate from Jacksonville, FL.

4. If you know California's state capital, then you know the hometown of the River Cats, a Triple-A affiliate for the Giants.

5. Teddy Roosevelt was once a member of this famed cavalry unit. Now, it is a Minor League Baseball Team in Frisco, TX.

7. This city is known for country music and legendary concert halls, like the Ryman Auditorium and the Grand Ole Opry. Its baseball team has a fitting name: the Sounds.

8. This team's name was the winner of a 2015 fan naming contest in Hartford, CT.

BALLPARK JUNK FOOD

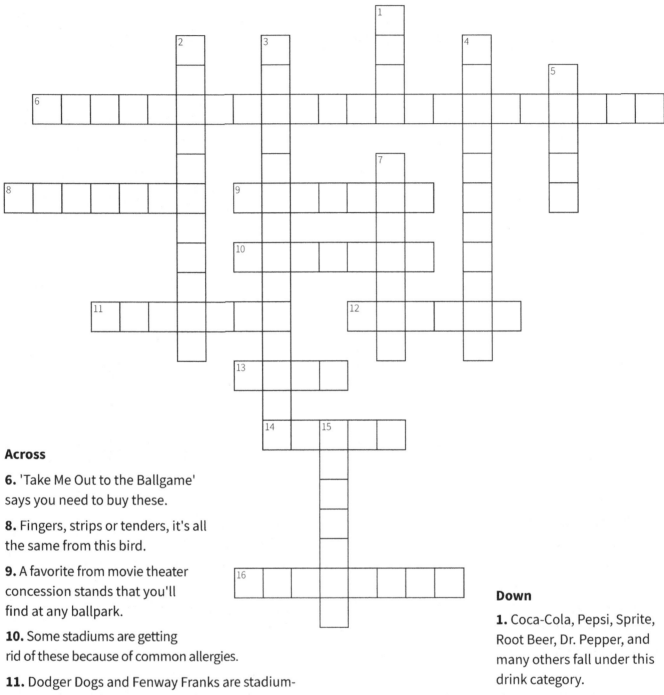

Across

6. 'Take Me Out to the Ballgame' says you need to buy these.

8. Fingers, strips or tenders, it's all the same from this bird.

9. A favorite from movie theater concession stands that you'll find at any ballpark.

10. Some stadiums are getting rid of these because of common allergies.

11. Dodger Dogs and Fenway Franks are stadium-specific names for this ballpark food.

12. Eating ice cream out of a small, plastic version of this protective equipment.

13. Miller, Budweiser, Coors, etc.

14. You can get this Japanese food consisting of cold, sticky rice, and raw fish at Yankee Stadium and other ballparks.

16. 11 Across dipped in batter and deep fried.

Down

1. Coca-Cola, Pepsi, Sprite, Root Beer, Dr. Pepper, and many others fall under this drink category.

2. Spun sugar, also known as fairy floss.

3. Players love to chew and spit these during the game.

4. Smother with cheese and chili or take the classic route and dip them in ketchup.

5. A must-have during a hot day game to stay hydrated.

7. A big, soft version of this crunchy and salty snack is great with mustard or cheese.

15. A special take on chili you'll only find in Cincinnati.

BIZARRE FOOD BASEBALL EDITION

1. Peanut Butter & Bacon Sandwich

2. Fritos Pie Corn Dog

3. Coney Dog Egg Roll

4. 18-Inch Breakfast Hot Dogs

5. Rocky Mountain Oyster Po'Boy

6. Chinese Food

7. Donut Burger

8. Slider Dog with Fruit Loops

9. Wisconsin Ultimate Cheese Fry

10. Pittsburgh Cone

11. Esquite

12. The Fowl Pole 2-Lb Chicken Tender

13. 32 Ingredient Salad

14. Toasted Grasshoppers

15. World Champions Burger (with replica World Series ring)

A. Progressive Field (Guardians)

B. Globe Life Field (Rangers)

C. T-Mobile Park (Mariners)

D. Target Field (Twins)

E. Chase Field (Diamondbacks)

F. PNC Park (Pirates)

G. Citizens Bank Park (Phillies)

H. Rogers Centre (Blue Jays)

I. Coors Field (Rockies)

J. Oracle Park (Giants)

K. Minute Maid Park (Astros)

L. Amer. Family Field (Brewers)

M. Dodger Stadium (Dodgers)

N. Truist Park (Braves)

O. Comerica Park (Tigers)

BASEBALL TRIVIA: *Never heard of a Rocky Mountain oyster? Since 1995, Coors Field has offered this delicacy. It's a sliced bull testicle battered and fried to a golden crisp! It may not be as popular as Rocky dogs or Helton burgers, but some fans keep coming back for these 'oysters.'*

TEAMS AND DIVISIONS

Fill in the missing teams from each division.

Hint: the teams are listed in alphabetical order within each division!

AMERICAN LEAGUE

EAST

Baltimore Orioles

Boston Red Sox

_____

Tampa Bay Rays

_____

CENTRAL

Chicago White Sox

_____

_____

Kansas City Royals

_____

WEST

_____

Los Angeles Angels

Oakland Athletics

_____

Texas Rangers

NATIONAL LEAGUE

EAST

_____

Philadelphia Phillies

_____

New York Mets

Washington Nationals

CENTRAL

_____

Cincinnati Reds

Milwaukee Brewers

Pittsburgh Pirates

_____

WEST

Arizona Diamondbacks

_____

Los Angeles Dodgers

_____

_____

BALLPARK CONSTRUCTION TIMELINE

Order the following ballparks in each group according to when they were built (oldest first).

GROUP A

_____ Kingdome

_____ Forbes Field

_____ Oracle Park

_____ Kauffman Stadium

_____ Wrigley Field

_____ Shea Stadium

_____ Polo Grounds

_____ (Old) Yankee Stadium

_____ Petco Park

_____ Minute Maid Park

_____ Fenway Park

_____ Ebbetts Field

_____ Coors Field

_____ RingCentral Coliseum

_____ Progressive Field

GROUP B

_____ Crosley Field

_____ Citi Field

_____ Comerica Park

_____ Dodger Stadium

_____ Candlestick Park

_____ Rogers Centre

_____ Three Rivers Stadium

_____ Turner Field

_____ Busch Stadium

_____ Citizens Bank Park

_____ New Yankee Stadium

_____ Tropicana Field

_____ Camden Yards

_____ Shibe Park

_____ Metrodome

TEAM NAME CHANGE

1. Colt .45's	**A.** Yankees
2. Browns	**B.** Reds
3. Senators	**C.** Twins
4. Expos	**D.** Red Sox
5. Indians	**E.** Astros
6. Red Stockings	**F.** Orioles
7. Brewers	**G.** Rangers
8. Pilots	**H.** Brewers
9. Senators	**I.** Nationals
10. Highlanders	**J.** Guardians
11. Americans	**K.** Cardinals

FUN FACT: *Few teams have undergone as many name changes as the Dodgers or Braves. The Atlanta Braves, as we know them today, were originally from Boston. They were called the Red Stockings, Doves, Rustlers, Braves, Bees, and — a popular favorite — Beaneaters. They moved to Milwaukee as the Braves before ultimately settling in Atlanta.*

Most fans know the Dodgers migrated from Brooklyn in 1957 to their current LA residence. However, did you know that the Dodgers also went by the Atlantics, Grays, Bridegrooms, Grooms, Superbas, and Robins?

DEMOLISHED DIAMONDS

```
C R W S K T N P S Y B M P G P Z W F V V B B S
O I U D M V A X K A K Y U S R H Q L O T W H A O
M V Q N I B W R T J D B P F C B X F S E T E G L
I E J U I S F E S I X X T A F S X I G G T A K Y
S R I O V H W G J R U U Z A E H H F H Y A K E M
K F I R F I K H D S T I W K X H R H M W Q Z A P
E R U G T B V V D C L S D Y S K T E Z S C S D I
Y O I O B E R U Y L H W A L T M T A Z K W H E C
P N I L Z P T G O E E N Z O E U E H B F B M J S
A T F O B A Y Y A V K I I Z R I J T U G O S U T
R S O P E R W S F E H D F N K Q F K R D Z Q S A
K T H Z A K T V E X L M E S T V I Y O O V X V D
O A X X G A Q S D E U R A T E N B R E Q D O Y I
J D H I D O T Y I Y F P F T G B T E L L A O R U
V I E I P A N F V I I Q V D F S R N Y C S H M M
Z U U L D B S V E M S B O K A N K O F C W O X E
D M E I D T D L Q B D M G P W R F W F R A G R F
P J U V E L D X V P E C V J C K L C O C V R Z C
J M U B R I T S Z K R A P K C I T S E L D N A C
X X B Z B U S C H M E M O R I A L S T A D I U M
E E E X H I B I T I O N S T A D I U M Z L X C J
Z M I E N O V N L J G I M O K S O H L A W T U W
X J N T J D K T D M L Y E P C G Y H A R C P T L
V C Y G O E T I G E R S T A D I U M U V X G X V
```

Riverfront Stadium	Polo Grounds	Turner Field
Busch Memorial Stadium	Forbes Field	Shea Stadium
Metrodome	Tiger Stadium	Olympic Stadium
Shibe Park	Crosley Field	Kingdome
Ebbets Field	Comiskey Park	Candlestick Park
Yankee Stadium	Astrodome	Exhibition Stadium

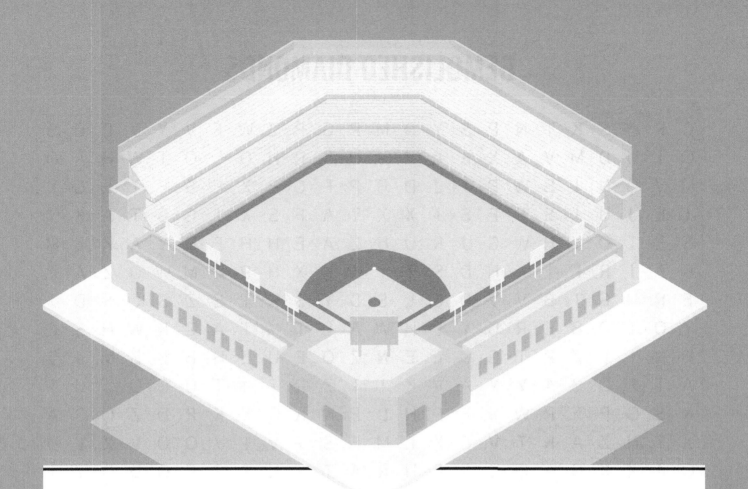

CHAPTER

4

JACKIE ROBINSON DAY

Every April 15th, we celebrate the spring day in 1947 when Jackie Robinson shattered baseball's color barrier. With his heroics on the field, Jackie set the stage for Civil Rights leaders like Dr. Martin Luther King Jr. to achieve a better, equal America. It was a rare occurrence when a sport, America's sport, led the country in social change.

This chapter highlights not only Jackie Robinson's life and impact on the United States of America, but also the achievements of the black players that were kept out of organized baseball.

NEGRO LEAGUE TEAMS

```
K N B N Z Q Y T S S V C A V Q M B E D U S P Q X
A X B B F S U V Z K J A G N C N H J T C N U O I
W F T Q E Q K S T N A I G N A B U C B A A S C N
L P U O N S G V N D N C Y S R K E A E J D H E S
O I W H O M E S T E A D G R A Y S A Q E I W N E
N T K J P U I M S C Z E O B B I G F R C Y O J S
F T U A O H I L L D A L E C L U B S A O R G T F
S S S Y N G C L C M M U S O Q Y I G R A V L Q B
R B N F M S Z P T T S T P V U H O K B L O G A Y
A U A B J F A M O X E A R S P A B K E U Z L Q U
T R B G Q R A S A R N F R M M L C Y I M T Z A H
S G U N Y P O C A Z A E E A A V S K I F L R E
A H C M M V L S I I T M R C L O S S M E M A S I
I C K U B Z R D B S T I K B P T K O U D D F L M
H R R I W X N D T S C Y M R A U R S H U G M R C
P A O S Y I A I C A A A M R H E E B N K H U O Z
L W Y O T S O D N N H W S O B S C J U A T Q A U
E F W A M R P G K G C H I L N H R E Q A A H Z H
D O E I T B I E N V I I A C Z A O H U P K U E E
A R N E M A E I P A O C I L N O R I C V E Z Z V
L D D U N S M W K G K X E L G J R C A W H B L K
I S F T V R F J L S N Y X Z L R J C H K G F A Q
H P Y Z I B J W O C T I M V B E F I S S I S T B
P G Z B A A V X U W B O E G F Z W H P E E U H U
```

Philadelphia Stars	Baltimore Black Sox	Hilldale Club
Indianapolis ABCs	New York Cubans	St Louis Stars
Detroit Stars	Memphis Red Sox	Birmingham Black Barons
New York Black Yankees	Homestead Grays	Pittsburgh Crawfords
Cuban Giants	Chicago American Giant	Kansas City Monarchs

FUN FACT: *The majority of Negro League clubs had black owners. Rube Foster and the other executives that founded the leagues wanted baseball to offer business opportunities to black communities.*

HISTORY OF JACKIE ROBINSON

Across

2. After his stint in the army, Jackie briefly coached this sport in Austin, Texas.

6. This jersey number was retired in 1997 by every Major League Baseball team in honor of Jackie Robinson.

8. It didn't take long for the Robinson family to move to this California town after Jackie was born.

9. Jackie Robinson Day takes place during this spring month and is a day when everyone in baseball wears the 42 on their jersey.

13. Robinson was an All-Star for how many years in a row?

15. While attending John Muir High School, Robinson received varsity letters in four sports: baseball, basketball, track and _____.

16. Jackie's birthplace in Georgia, which shares the name of Egypt's capital.

18. Robinson got his first professional baseball job when this Kansas City Negro League team signed him.

19. Jackie met his future wife in college. What was her name?

Down

1. On April 15, 1947, Jackie Robinson stepped onto this field in Brooklyn and officially broke baseball's color barrier.

3. Robinson won this award in 1947 given to the best new player in the league.

4. At age 53, Robinson passed away at his home in this New England state.

5. In 1945, Robinson was interviewed by this Brooklyn Dodgers executive who was looking for a black player to introduce into the all-white Major Leagues.

7. in 1955, Robinson and the Dodgers won the World Series over their cross-town rivals, the New York _____.

10. Robinson was drafted into the army during the second one of these, but he never saw combat.

11. In 1949, Jackie won this award (abbreviated) for the National League's best overall player.

12. Athleticism ran in the family. Jackie's brother received this type of medal at the 1936 Olympics in Berlin for track and field.

14. Jackie was first assigned to this Canadian team in Montreal.

17. in 1939, Robinson enrolled in this CA college (abbreviated), where he lettered in all four sports again, the first Bruin to do so.

WHO SAID IT? JACKIE ROBINSON EDITION

1. "Jackie's character was much more important than his batting average."

2. "To do what he did has got to be the most tremendous thing I've ever seen in sports."

3. "Jackie Robinson made my success possible. Without him, I would never have been able to do what I did."

4. "A credit to baseball and to America."

5. "Jackie Robinson made his country and you and me and all of us a shadow more free."

6. "He's the reason I'm here. Jackie was a trailblazer, and we all owe him a lot. He's the reason I put on this uniform every day."

7. "A life is not important except in the impact it has on other lives."

A. Dr. Martin Luther King Jr.

B. Hank Aaron

C. Pee Wee Reese

D. Branch Rickey

E. Jackie Robinson

F. Roger Kahn

G. Tim Anderson

FUN FACT: *Jackie Robinson's path was never easy, a point he punctuated with his biography entitled* I Never Had It Made. *Aside from death threats and slurs from fans, Robinson faced turmoil from teammates and other players, even off the field.*

When members of the Dodgers began forming a petition stating they wouldn't play alongside Robinson, it prompted Leo Durocher to say, "I don't care if the guy is yellow or black, or if he has stripes like a god-damn zebra. I'm the manager of this team and I say he plays."

Other teams attempted to boycott games against the Dodgers, resulting in another quotable remark. This time it was Ford Frick, president of the National League, who spoke up. "I don't care if it wrecks the National League for five years. This is the United States of America."

BREAKING THE COLOR BARRIER

1. The last player to wear the number 42 before it was retired by all of Major League Baseball was Mariano Rivera.

TRUE	FALSE

2. Jackie Robinson was the first African-American to play at the major league level.

TRUE	FALSE

3. Jackie Robinson won the first ever Rookie of the Year award.

TRUE	FALSE

4. Dodgers manager Leo Durocher despised Jackie Robinson.

TRUE	FALSE

5. When Negro League clubs and Major League Baseball teams faced one another in exhibitions, the major leaguers won most of the time.

TRUE	FALSE

6. Who was the other black player to join Robinson in the 1947 season, breaking the color barrier for the American League?

A. Satchel Paige	**B.** Roberto Clemente	**C.** Larry Doby	**D.** Hank Aaron

7. This player was an outspoken advocate for Negro Leaguers' eligibility into the Hall of Fame.

A. Sandy Koufax	**B.** Mickey Mantle	**C.** Ty Cobb	**D.** Ted Williams

8. Which Major League Baseball team was the last to integrate black players on their roster?

A. Detroit Tigers	**B.** Atlanta Braves	**C.** New York Yankees	**D.** Boston Red Sox

9. This player was the first to be inducted into the Hall of Fame solely on his performance in the Negro Leagues.

A. Josh Gibson	**B.** Satchel Paige	**C.** Cool Papa Bell	**D.** Larry Doby

10. This team fielded the first all-black starting roster.

A. Detroit Tigers	**B.** St. Louis Cardinals	**C.** Pittsburgh Pirates	**D.** Cleveland Indians

JACKIE ROBINSON TRIVIA

1. What position did Jackie play?

| **A.** Catcher | **B.** 2nd Base | **C.** Pitcher | **D.** Designated Hitter |

2. What year was Robinson inducted into the Hall of Fame?

| **A.** 1955 | **B.** 1960 | **C.** 1962 | **D.** He was never inducted |

3. When and where did Jackie Robinson break the color barrier?

| **A.** February 13, 1939, at Ebbets Field | **B.** April 15, 1955, at Yankees Stadium | **C.** April 15, 1997, at Wrigley Field | **D.** April 15, 1947, at Ebbets Field |

4. While Robinson was born in Georgia, most of his childhood was spent in this California city near LA.

| **A.** Pasadena | **B.** San Francisco | **C.** Glendale | **D.** San Diego |

5. Branch Rickey was known for keeping his mouth clean. Yet, he sat Jackie down after signing him and threw every swear word he could think of at the man. Why did he do this?

| **A.** He wanted to impress Jackie by swearing | **B.** He hated Robinson and wanted him to know it | **C.** To prepare Jackie for everything he would hear and face on the field | **D.** He just wanted to try out swearing for once |

6. There were many black baseball stars worthy of being the first. One in particular was very outspoken and felt he had been snubbed by Jackie Robinson. Who was he?

| **A.** Josh Gibson | **B.** Cool Papa Bell | **C.** Oscar Charleston | **D.** Satchel Paige |

7. Branch Rickey is known for signing Jackie Robinson, but who was the manager at the time for the Brooklyn Dodgers?

| **A.** Leo Durocher | **B.** Vin Scully | **C.** Tommy Lasorda | **D.** Dave Roberts |

8. This fellow Dodger reportedly put his arm around Jackie Robinson during a game to show fans that he stood with his teammate, despite the color of his skin.

| **A.** Dixie Walker | **B.** Pee Wee Reese | **C.** Eddie Stanky | **D.** Leo Durocher |

STARS OF THE NEGRO LEAGUES

```
R U E G D I R D N A D Y A R B B B W J G D I D P G
O C A F X B N T P M H X W F P I G O U P C Y Y S
C T I U D L N W Q G C Z F F L F X E O D N A V H
M B O H K A R W Z R L S Q L O I I S S N I J G J
E A G N I E V R G D E O I P D V A M C H V B Z V
L U R U O L M U E Y L E Y K X G A O A U I O Y A
E T X T D S L M D T W D F U B T X K R V C K F M
D E U R I Y B Q C E S E Z W Q W V E C W F G X A
B T G N X N H I L I D O N D W J N Y H Y J F P F
G V G I Y M D L G F S I F W J U T W A W J Z G S
H R R J A S S I S H V P M E W I Q I R Q N G M I
U L G L V P Z W H R S V R L B O W L L K E P R D
L N P K O F L Q I I J O J Z D U A L E X W D E S
W S R I I H C E I Z G G J F J A R I S H D G Q J
U O V V V Y T D H X W O G U K Q N A T K B K O Q
S G B G Y N Y X A C T K D J R B U M O X E E J R
J H X J O O T K X Y T Y X X T X O S N S R Q B Z
Y O L M L L X K G J A T N S L K J T O Y B P J
G B J L G Q Q O Q O V L S U V Y C F G R C Z Y H
G W P Z Q H X Z H J F S Y U A W I A Y Q F Q R D
J O B Q M U H N O M X I A F D Q N B Z W I C B S
P G O H F Y S C O O L P A P A B E L L G N S K D
J N K X D O Z K W W R E C D R A N O E L K C U B
S B H Z N Q S G X C I K R Y B I L L B O S T E R
```

Ray Dandridge	Pop Lloyd	Buck Leonard
Bill Boster	Joe Rogan	Monte Irvin
Willie Wells	Rube Foster	Satchel Paige
Judy Johnson	Martin Dihigo	Josh Gibson
Oscar Charleston	Cool Papa Bell	Joe Smokey Williams

BASEBALL COLOR BARRIER TIMELINE

Match the year to the major event in the baseball color barrier timeline.

_____ Jackie Robinson starts on Opening Day and breaks the color barrier.

_____ Bob Watson becomes the first black General Manager.

_____ Rube Foster founds the Negro National League with other black business owners.

_____ Little League Baseball integrates their teams for youth players.

_____ Frank Robinson becomes the first black manager in Major League Baseball.

_____ The last MLB team integrates its roster.

_____ The Pittsburgh Pirates field an all-black lineup, including Roberto Clemente and Willie Stargell.

_____ Pearl Harbor is bombed, sending the US into World War II.

_____ Major League Baseball gives Negro League players major league status, entering their stats and names into the official record books.

_____ The #42 is retired by all MLB teams in honor of Jackie Robinson.

_____ Branch Rickey signs Jackie Robinson to the Brooklyn Dodgers, sending him first to Montreal.

_____ Larry Doby signs with the Cleveland Indians, breaking the color barrier in the American League.

_____ The Rookie of the Year award is renamed in Jackie Robinson's honor as the first to receive the honor.

WORD BANK

1920	1955	1987
1939	1959	1994
1945	1971	1997
1947	1975	2020

NEGRO LEAGUES MYTHOLOGY

1. This Negro League catcher threw Ty Cobb out on multiple plays during an exhibition game. Cobb was so enraged he demanded the distance between each base be checked for accuracy.

A. Satchel Paige

2. In Pittsburgh, this slugger hit a ball so high and far, no one could see it come down. The next day, a ball mysteriously fell from the sky and landed in an outfielder's glove, making everyone assume it was the ball hit the day before finally returning to earth.

B. Cristóbal Torriente

3. A player with such speed he reportedly could run the bases in 12 seconds flat. Satchel Paige once said the player would turn the lights off and be in bed, under the covers before the room got dark.

C. Cool Papa Bell

4. During the Negro World Series, this legendary pitcher intentionally walked multiple batters in a one-run game to get to the opposing team's best slugger, Josh Gibson. He struck him out.

D. Josh Gibson

5. Not only did this individual help found the Negro National League, but he also once engineered a significant rally involving 11 bunts in a row.

E. Rube Foster

6. This catcher earned the nickname "Double Duty" when he caught a shutout in the first game of a double header before taking his gear off and pitching a shutout in the second game.

F. Ted Radcliffe

7. Babe Ruth went to Cuba once to play some exhibition baseball. However, it was this local player who stole the show with three home runs and a double off Ruth himself.

G. Bruce Petway

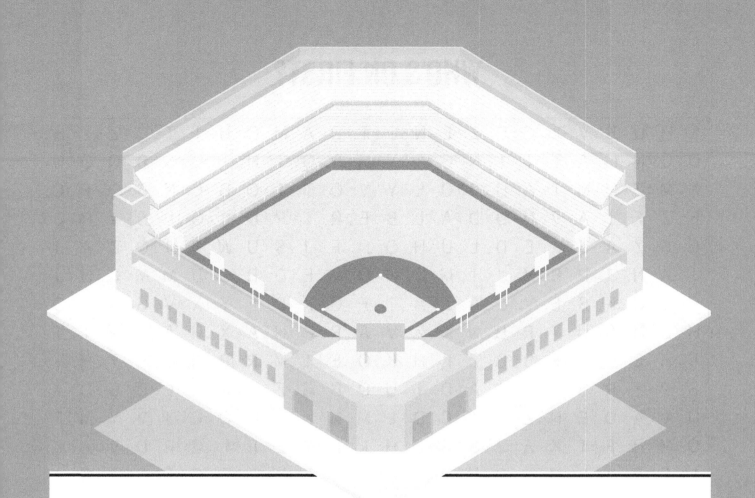

CHAPTER

5

THE MIDSUMMER CLASSIC

The Midsummer Classic is Major League Baseball's all-star game. It marks the midpoint in the season and a brief break from regular play. The game's greatest hitters, pitchers, and fielders from each league come together to slug it out in one of baseball's most exciting events. You won't find more talent on the field than The Midsummer Classic.

The best players from every position participate in The Midsummer Classic. This chapter of puzzles and games focuses on baseball's greatest athletes to ever play the game.

WHO'S ON FIRST?

```
C H U B V L C C Z E N I T R A M O N I T Q Z Z H
D O N M A T T I N G L Y M D Q T H T U S B Q Q U
X M Z H M T A U J O E Y V O T T O B C N G O F C
K Z F I A V N D D A L B E R T P U J O L S V R D
G K Z A J R E D L U H Q H F J S U W T J O D A J
I A N J R B M J I M T H O M E D R G D M Y C N J
R G H K S E V O A F A I F G X D L Y X V G P K Q
H D H S U Y R B N N Z V A R G H A X H A F R T T
E H E G I F B B Z K H K Q E I M R R N D A T H V
G P T R S A A A D I U D B G Z B A H L B G O A
U V A D E N Z R T C D L M N X J M O C J V Y M F
O M B F I K A J S G L H L E Y E P L G P D V A L
L S R A Y M L G U U Z E E E E Y L S G G E J S A
U T I U G S H E T W U S U R B I O L O Z P O Y W
R A B M E T H C E L D W F G W R N Y I B G I A M
O N O M B L N U S L M E X K I Z E M L U F S R M
R M E Y N K T O C D I D C N W M Y W X Q J D R V
M U H E H I K S S D L J E A U N P W P W P Y S U H
F S S R P U A P D N Y O V H N N Y O B K Q M N
W I J F S D I E S Y A K G H M G N T E X N A E R
Z A Q S B U R P R E U P O L V C T C S H S Z I Y
A L G H P F B M U O P J A Y U U P D G X D B D E
U J E F F B A G W E L L G C A A C Y I P R K D D
B F U A N T H O N Y R I Z Z O V P G T I Z G E E
```

Hank Greenberg	Derek Lee	Don Mattingly
Johnny Mize	Stan Musial	Miguel Cabrera
Will Clark	Harmon Killebrew	Albert Pujols
Paul Goldschmidt	Jim Thome	Lou Gehrig
Tino Martinez	Joey Votto	Jeff Bagwell
Eddie Murray	Freddie Freeman	Frank Thomas
Cap Anson	Anthony Rizzo	

ALL-STAR SECOND BASEMEN

1. PNA JOILEA
_____

2. YERN RBDSEAGN
_____

3. EIACJK NORSONIB
_____

4. ASHCE YTLEU
_____

5. UNTIDS DIEAPRO
_____

6. FFEJ TKNE
_____

7. CGIAR BGIGIO
_____

8. IDEED SLNILOC
_____

9. RROGES YHRBNSO
_____

10. OEJ GARNMO
_____

11. ORD RCAWE
_____

12. EOSJ ULETAV
_____

13. YBBBO RGHCI
_____

14. HLACREI RIEGNGERH
_____

"Not a lot of guys get to play their whole careers with one team because of the economics of this game. I can't think of a better time to be wearing an Astros uniform."

– Craig Biggio, Hall of Fame Second Baseman

NATIONAL & AMERICAN LEAGUE HISTORY

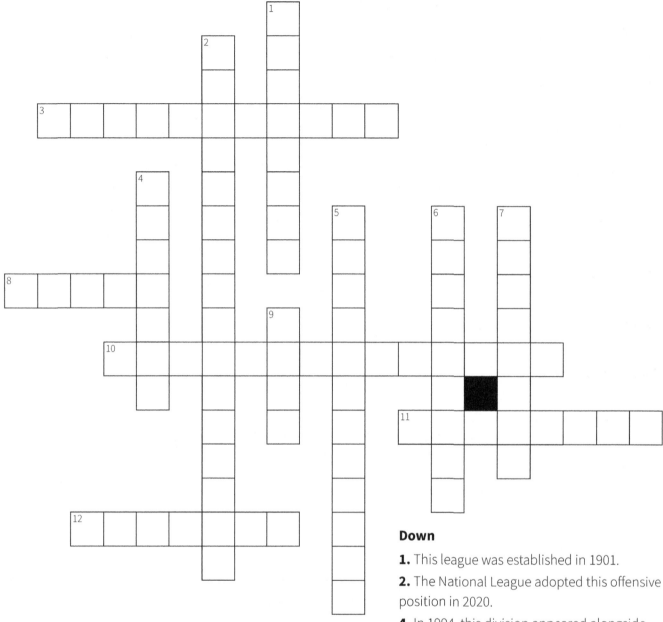

Down

1. This league was established in 1901.

2. The National League adopted this offensive position in 2020.

4. In 1994, this division appeared alongside the standard east and west.

5. The latest new team to join the Nation League (not just a team relocating).

6. This team was one of the charter franchises of the American League. However, they went by the "Blues" back then.

7. This baseball commissioner saw the introduction of the Wild Card to the playoff format and regular season interleague play.

9. In 1962, the National League expanded to include the Houston Colt .45s and this New York team.

Across

3. The first all-star game between the American and National leagues happened in 1903.

8. Originally, the National League consisted of this number of teams.

10. In 1969, the Montreal Expos and this team joined the ranks of the National League.

11. This league was founded in 1876.

12. In 1997, this team moved from the American League to the National League.

FIND THE COMMON THREAD

1. Mike Trout, Giancarlo Stanton, Jose Altuve, and Trevor Story.

---

2. George Springer, Stephen Strasburg, Jorge Soler, and Corey Seager.

---

3. Tommy Pham, Juan Soto, Christian Yelich, and Sandy Alcantara.

---

4. Bryce Harper, Pete Alonso, Aaron Judge, and Giancarlo Stanton.

---

5. Yadier Molina, Salvador Perez, Yasmani Grandal, and Jorge Alfaro.

---

6. Nolan Arenado, Manny Machado, Brian Anderson, and Josh Donaldson.

---

7. Cavan Biggio, Vladimir Guerrero Jr, Bo Bichette, and Cody Bellinger.

---

8. Cal Raleigh, Julio Rodriguez, Mitch Haniger, and Ty France.

---

9. Robbie Ray, Justin Verlander, Corbin Burnes, and Jacob deGrom (besides being pitchers)

---

10. Jurickson Profar, Ozzie Albies, Kenley Jansen, and Andrelton Simmons.

OUTFIELDERS FROM LEFT TO RIGHT

```
G R U R R M S G A N S R D F S R V Q M O F R O U V
L X O V E P W Y O E A U B L U K H Z D D P D Y N
J T O F M T F E A O K T W L E T I M R A I N E S
N R E N O S H E S M S T X D A I U U N T F L B W
D B Y O N L E G L V E E X A S R F B T O L I K Z
S B N K T L I Y U T H I G J O Y R N L B S R I R
T O O T E M S X G A N L L O R W I Y I W Q W O M
O C R A I S S W P Y L A S L S I V U W W T B D Q
N Y A N R C J I G M E S M Q I L A O W A E P W M
Y T A A V W K R Y V Z K S Y K W I V G R L V Z W
G J K G I U I G W C E L W O E Y T N T F Y K A R
W K N A N D R E D A W S O N N K J O R G X J E D
Y G A J I S B I S J F R P C B E C A R M O E S R
N J H N G T Y P I F A K M R J L N I C J H X M J
N E A F H T P D L L F U U K E K S T M D A R A Y
I Q R O M R U E P H A W P M R N G T E V C R I E
F X S S T I C H Y Y H M E O B W T N T C D B L F
I T T S K Q K I G H J N B J I M R I C E O W L F
J Z T Y N I E U E M T I R R U V D B O Z N Y I I
J D Q O N L T P W E N U T S N L R N K S H C W R
M W B E L C T I K S M E Z R T S A Y L R A C D G
N P R E R E S Z O K C O R B U O L K L V V K E N
I O C H Z W M N M C M S N R A Q N J T L W I T E
L L E B A P A P L O O C T R I S S P E A K E R K
```

Andre Dawson	Tony Gwynn	Willie Mays	Tim Raines
Enos Slaughter	Roberto Clemente	Kirby Puckett	Ralph Kiner
Larry Walker	Hank Aaron	Mickey Mantle	Monte Irvin
Dave Winfield	Tris Speaker	Carl Yastrzemski	Goose Goslin
Frank Robinson	Cool Papa Bell	Jim Rice	Lou Brock
Mel Ott	Ty Cobb	Ted Williams	Ken Griffey Jr.

SHORTSTOPS ON TOP

1. LCA NPREKI JR _____

2. MORA LVZUQIE _____

3. EZIZO IHTSM _____

4. RNEIE ABNKS _____

5. EPE EEW SREEE _____

6. ROYT ITLZUTWKOI _____

7. AYBRR RNLKAI _____

8. SNUHO NGERAW _____

9. ERKED TERJE _____

10. BORIN TUNOY _____

11. ULSI OCRAIIAP _____

12. NCORCIFSA ORLNID _____

13. LOU BEUDAORU _____

14. BO CETIEHBT _____

15. AALN EMMTLALR _____

BASEBALL TRIVIA: *Despite pitchers throwing balls over 100 mph (and batters hitting them even harder), only one player has ever died playing baseball. His name was Ray Chapman, a shortstop for Cleveland. He was struck in the head by an incoming pitch.*

At the time, pitchers would purposefully dirty the ball to make it harder to see. Spectators claimed Chapman never even saw it coming and the sound was loud enough that players and fans alike thought it may have hit the bat.

Chapman took a few steps toward first base, collapsed, and later died in the hospital. The Cleveland Indians went on to win the World Series that year in his honor.

THE HOT CORNER

G T A F T H U Q R Q A Q S J F G Y T R G G N K L
E R T L E B N A I R D A U O H G S D B F K Y F E
B K P N H V V P M M D N G S J O W E H U T B N Q
Y H N R T H S Y C X V C Y T D I M H C S E K I M
X S E L T T E N G I A R G G S G A B S T J P A A
Y H R N G N H R K J K Q C S G U I W R T V S R R
R L W O O A P C C D T V H B X C E O F E H C E U
N O S N I B O R S K O O R B N H D O V R W O G T
H U B A N H X P N H U X L I T A O A R B S T A N
W P W D S D X J U A H I M A N Q N W R E N T E E
D B F C K K S D X U M E U L L H N G I R S V
V T O G J Z C R Y V E E R Q O C O O D R G O E N
J O I D K V Y Q Y R I A L N S L J W D O N L L I
U I T M S F V W M D N G G L U R L U V E H E Y B
M K M N W Q T U D A M O O P E G H E L G G N K O
I E I M A A F E L J R D Z P T G K C B S O P S R
K N C Z Y S L O X I G E P Y H X F Y W W R Q I
E B R J T C N L A J L I P J H Z L R S T D B P T
L O L W D O O A U H H X C G V T W R A S D D C S
O Y Y G L B E L R C D W A D E B O G G S U S U F
W E I G Y T I P L T H G I R W D I V A D Q T O B
E R B L A X G F S I V D C Q A L R B F I U Z L A
L K W Y S I I X V T N V P Z A R Z O G I F U I K
L M D A S L Q Y Y O N S M A I Y W H V K F Y Q T

Tim Wallach	Evan Longoria	Nolan Arenado
Kyle Seager	Jimmy Collins	Adrian Beltre
Mike Lowell	Eddie Mathews	George Brett
Robin Ventura	Ron Santo	Wade Boggs
David Wright	Graig Nettles	Brooks Robinson
Ken Boyer	Mike Schmidt	Chipper Jones
Buddy Bell	Scott Rolen	

ALL-STAR GAME MOMENTS

Across

2. This player hit the first inside-the-park home run during the All-Star Game in 2007.

3. This "Mr. October" player hit a 520-foot home run that is still the longest hit in All-Star Game history.

5. This player hit a solo home run in his final Midsummer Classic appearance and got to play at his natural shortstop position, with a little encouragement from Alex Rodriguez.

8. This city hosted the 2002 All-Star Game, which had a controversial outcome when it ended in a tie.

9. This player robbed Barry Bonds of a home run during the 2002 All-Star Game, promoting the slugger to jokingly storm out to centerfield and toss the player over his shoulder.

10. While pitching at his home park in the 1999 All Star Game, this pitcher struck out five batters in just two innings of work.

Down

1. In 1978, this player hit two triples in the Midsummer Classic. He's the only player to achieve this.

4. It took exactly 50 years of All Star Games for the first grand slam to happen, which was hit by this player.

6. Catcher Ray Fosse dislocated his shoulder after a rough collision at home from this player during the 1970 All Star Game.

7. This legendary slugger hit the very first home run in the history of All-Star games.

CY YOUNG STARS

```
P Z J E N I V A L G M O T T P R K R F Y L Z R M
G E Z A F S L G E L D F G Z C X A H D S E H A F
I I D C C Y N F D W I R H O Y K X H Q D M W F B
Y S E R Q O U U R V E X E S K U S M N P S M N B
D U T L O P B E D G P E B T H I I A K Y J H A Z
Z X M E O M V D M O H U D N H A N O J N A R R F
T U R E V A A A E I N R V H V R H N K P T W P J
O T F Y E E D R R G O N M Z E K O Y S O H Y L H
C Z A S S D C B T E R X E H W S G N L I G U M G
L T M R U X S A U I T O X W N W E O T J H M J C
I O Z Z R A R S R Y N I M H C R C E E U S N Q S
T E R T W F E O K L L E O O R O Y T C S V F N B
N W E J L U D E L E T J Z A L F M Z U T F A G O
B L I D V O V A F L Y O W O O R P B A I C T R B
J L F S K X C O D E X N R R N G E E N C V N G
E I S P B Y S E N D F F D M Y V Q Q I V S R R I
R F G U E D P A C T H Z I D E E N Q U E Z E N B
K G T C G N R A O L L N J N D N O Y V R M A V S
V B L E T A D M G M Y D N M G L X W T L U R V O
P O B S S S Y A B S G P L Y J E D V A A J R L N
B T J B S N E M E L C R E G O R R P N N E Z I V
O E W A H S R E K N O T Y A L C M S P D R B R S
G A Y L O R D P E R R Y R D B I G N X E I L U U
Q H J K E S T X C Q Q T F X J N Z B C R I X I Y
```

Jacob deGrom	Whitey Ford	Tom Glavine
Clayton Kershaw	Sandy Koufax	Pedro Martinez
Roger Clemens	Tom Seaver	Randy Johnson
Rolle Fingers	Gaylord Perry	Bartolo Colon
Bob Gibson	Jim Palmer	Justin Verlander
Don Newcombe	Steve Carlton	Felix Hernandez
Warren Spahn	Greg Maddux	

GREATEST BEHIND THE PLATE

```
E P C R O Y C A M P A N E L L A Q K Y N J F E R
N G S N Q O A M G X W Y W V F O I M O F L F T A
A D W P K J P C W A C N P F S P I O G F U C S B
R I V I C R C T L Z R U O E J K J V I F R O C V
H S D C L Y T W M S Y Y Q S E T M F B S R J K S
C Y L F I Q O P J E V G C P N H F X E B E T C Z
O C L C I S S O S U E Z I A H U K B R Y F B E D
C A W G Q K E O K C D A N S R E M R R F J U Y B
Y C M Y I M P R X A Z I N L T T Y N A U G L Q I
E S R S A R B A I Z L O R I V D E B A I R K F X
K V N U E D M R A O M S R L M A R R M Z E U R
C I E T J O C R M M Q A D B H L Y D Z H R Y C Q
I R S V B J G R I Y V R D I B Y O E E H T U K E
M U R J X K E S P N X C X R I R J K R T R V H M
B Y H Y E I D R O B C I I C N H N V E S N I S T
D M O Z D E Z S I B M F O A E O L J P G H K P M
M T Y A T X A C A Q X B V E G Y D C R X Z C F H
I C Y D R J J L C N Q Y I S R H J H R O W M D Y X
D M Y T V I C T O R M A R T I N E Z D I L O Y J
E T I P X H C N E B Y N N H O J H D A R X K D G
L N J L J S A M V M E K J Z F I L H V A K V Q X
A D A S O P E G R O J M N R Q U T P L X C S S O
G B K S I F N O T L R A C P L U Z F A Z B R T C
M O G A I T N A S O T I N E B O B U S O O S N W
```

Benito Santiago	Mickey Cochrane	Roy Campanella
Ted Simmons	Jorge Posada	Buster Posey
Jason Varitek	Mike Piazza	Thurman Munson
Victor Martinez	Yogi Berra	Yadier Molina
Gary Carter	Carlton Fisk	Ivan Rodriguez
Joe Mauer	Salvador Perez	Johnny Bench

BEST OF THE AL

```
H R I Z E U G I R D O R O I L U J D J L Q P T K
G I X A A R O N J U D G E D F P G I R G M K V E
Y E Q A I L J U S T I N V E R L A N D E R N D
W C V R H P G H K Z Z A F S X M S Y C B R B Y N
D A T U E B M F X V X U G P C J D S C V B Z E K
D N O A T G V O N K O A H H V X Y Y G Y R P S J
C D K D R L N F T U Z K E V G F H C J A K H O R
J X Z G J E A I S A F K I R P C G O F V O T Q R
A G M U O T V E R E L J I K R I D A J H U G L P
O X Z Z R V M H S P I E O N S O E G E Q Q I O M
G C E W E M F G J O S T K T D L C I I R Y J G O
H I R J R E T S T T J E R M D X O S S L K G Z O
P J I Q R D Y Y W J I M G E A H O F O V S K Z K
A C M H E X M R K V O M V R T N C L H L D X D J
Z A A B U M M O N V E A A O G O J H H R O L G
A R R Q G T E Y C Q R S N N Y E C A P H M A L R
C M E O R X T Z P S P I J I D N G F H O I U C T
Q Q S O I S G E R R I T C O L E Q Y H M K S J Q
B Q O D M I M Q F M H Q V B X I R B W A E T F B
J O J U I N O T X U B N O R Y B K S D Y T A U G
M K I K D O H A S G F W O F U S W T O T R F B
C M E T A H R K S A N F T J T I L V J N O A J V
D D O I L D M D M Z G J Z A B G J B R W U J L Y
E T P Q V O C J I D T Z E S W E E D T T T V N D
```

Rafael Devers

George Springer

Justin Verlander

Alek Manoah

Gerrit Cole

Byron Buxton

Julio Rodriguez

Jose Ramirez

Carlos Correa

Jose Altuve

Shohei Ohtani

Mike Trout

Aaron Judge

Tim Anderson

Vladimir Guerrero Jr

BEST OF THE NL

```
L Z W D I K X U N C D F E P C D X Z H S I J I S
T S Z T Q U N S M R F T R I O B A L M X Y D G D
Z O Q Z F P J F F Z R T D D S I S B E B J E X C
A H Z N E X F G A A B Z P H D T H X R A R D D K
B U Q Z F L X M M E H F Q N T D D Y K T E R T T
T R J D I N D G E T Z L I E S A C T J D N G T B
T O A M L E N F D M C W B O A E L B T I R A I L
Q J D J D I A T D I D E J X H R H Q B M U Y Z V
S K N U L U H L V E I B H A N B R B R H T W Z F
Y G J R O I Q M B K D K R A J N V M S C A A O O
K Z A U X J D O O I Y P F S L L R R E S E H D Y
Q T W Q A D J O Y P E Z T Y A O G F D R S A A A
S B U I A N M C P R Q S B Y N A F W F L T R H B
I B J Q U Y S T W H O O E A B V W W O O N E C M
C U O X M F R O D Z W H L W F F V A Y G K A W
V G S V A B P G T I P D F B W P B S T L K N M C
L M H I J A G K L O A E D B Q B K W X U R O Y V
Y F H R E J A Z Z C H I S H O L M J R A I T N D
Q J A P F Q S Y U X R H N W Y T A E E P R I N O
Y M D L E Z D N Q N F Y A B E L M C V A Q A A H
X U E P M Y A R B A M G F M T F A Q D E K L M V
C X R O V J F W S L M H N S K C H Z K S Z C D W
F F D U R X S A N D Y A L C A N T A R A D B U B
H D V X G U Y R A L B E R T P U J O L S H Q S N
```

Ozzie Albies	Josh Hader	Ronald Acuna Jr
Manny Machado	Edwin Diaz	Mookie Betts
Trea Turner	Starling Marte	Bryce Harper
Sandy Alcantara	Juan Soto	Jazz Chisholm Jr
Clayton Kershaw	Albert Pujols	Paul Goldschmidt

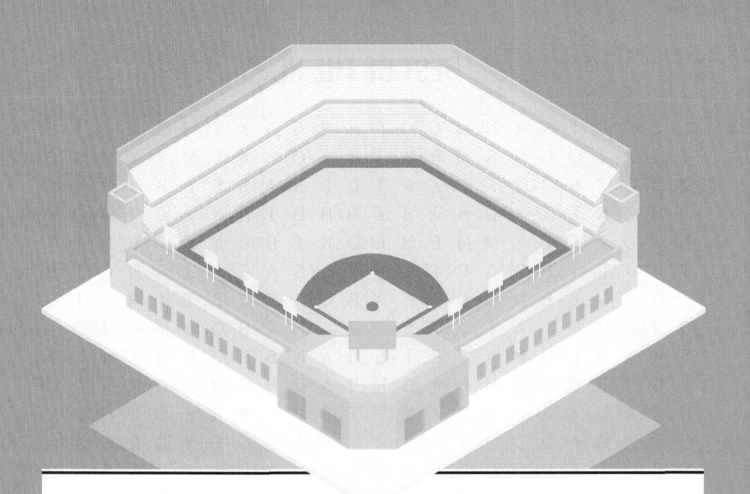

CHAPTER

6

THE HOME RUN DERBY

During MLB's All-Star break, the game's biggest and best sluggers take center stage for The Home Run Derby. In one night, more than a hundred balls fly over the outfield walls and into the hands of waiting fans. It's one of the most exciting and jaw-dropping spectacles in baseball.

To make it to The Home Run Derby, you must be a seriously good hitter. This section of puzzles, games, and trivia is all about hitters and home runs.

SERIOUS SLUGGERS

1. KNE EIFYGRF JR   _____

2. RABYR NBOSD   _____

3. MDILAVIR URREGEOR   _____

4. BLREAT OLUJSP   _____

5. YSMMA SOAS   _____

6. RAKM MGCREIW   _____

7. EBBA HRTU   _____

8. UOL GEHGIR   _____

9. ROANHM LIBLWREKE   _____

10. EWILLI YMAS   _____

11. EMIJIM XXOF   _____

12. KHNA ARONA   _____

FUN FACT: *Expos' scout Fred Ferreira signed Vladimir Guerrero as a totally unknown player for $10,000. Sports Illustrated lists it as the second-best deal in baseball history after the Yankees trading for Babe Ruth from the Red Sox.*

Ferreira was in the Dominican Republic checking on Guerrero's progress when the player asked him if he was mad. Guerrero was hitting last and thought he was being cut. The scout laughed and told him he was making him hit last because he was losing all the balls.

HOME RUN DERBY WINNERS

1. Bryce Harper		**A.** 2011
2. Robinson Cano		**B.** 2022
3. Giancarlo Stanton		**C.** 2016
4. Pete Alonso		**D.** 2015
5. Yoenis Cespedes		**E.** 2005
6. Juan Soto		**F.** 2017
7. Aaron Judge		**G.** 2006
8. Todd Frazier		**H.** 2019 & 2021
9. Prince Fielder		**I.** 2008
10. Ken Griffey Jr.		**J.** 1997
11. Garret Anderson		**K.** 2009 & 2012
12. Vladimir Guerrero		**L.** 1996
13. Jason Giambi		**M.** 2002
14. David Ortiz		**N.** 2018
15. Justin Morneau		**O.** 2004
16. Barry Bonds		**P.** 1994, 1998 & 1999
17. Sammy Sosa		**Q.** 2003
18. Bobby Abreu		**R.** 2000
19. Luis Gonzalez		**S.** 2001
20. Tino Martinez		**T.** 2013 & 2014
21. Ryan Howard		**U.** 2010
22. Miguel Tejada		**V.** 2007

MEMORABLE DERBY MOMENTS

Across

6. The 1990 Home Run Derby was an embarrassing showcase when this many players failed to get a single home run.

9. In 2021, this slugger set a first-round record with 35 home runs.

10. This player beat Todd Frazier in the final round of the 2016 Home Run Derby.

11. In 2002, this player reportedly hit seven home runs that measured over 500 feet, including one at 524 feet, which is a Derby record.

12. Despite Josh Hamilton's mammoth first-round performance, this player ultimately won the 2008 Derby.

Down

1. Josh Hamilton belted this many home runs in the opening round of the 2008 Derby at Yankee Stadium.

2. In 1998, Ken Griffey Jr. became the first player to win multiple Home Run Derby titles. He reportedly wasn't going to participate, but a conversation with this Hall of Fame player and manager changed his mind.

3. Vladimir Guerrero Jr. and this player went through three swing-off tiebreakers to decide who would face Pete Alonso in the Derby finals.

4. Players from both leagues gave this individual a standing ovation in the middle of his first-round Derby performance in 2022.

5. The first Home Run Derby happened in 1985 at the Metrodome. Dave Parker won with only this many home runs.

7. Not only did this rookie hit 52 homers in his first season, but he also won the 2017 Home Run Derby.

8. This three-time Derby winner didn't take the trophy home in 1993, but he did manage to hit the B&O warehouse across the street from Camden Yards. No player before or after has come close to repeating the feat.

HITTING FOR AVERAGE

```
T L W O P M D O S C A R C H A R L E S T O N I M
O D L R O B E R T O C L E M E N T E G L O G Z H
N P R I I C H I R O S U Z U K I X J X X X Z X X G
Y P H H G M Z H K L J B T F J B H T U R E B A B
G M P X J P Z H U S H A N K A A R O N C N X M O
W G S A K H D J W E R A C D O R W Z F H I M B S
Y X S M U W L Q R B K W G C N P I G W O T Y J E
N T N H Q L M E I I B W K U J U L P O L R N I N
N R O O M M Y L H V O Q U F N L C B Y A E L R R
V I Y T S E W O A G O O C W P L I P Q B M P P A
C S G E P L L T L B L N Y Y U N E V S S R Z I E
E S A D H C I E J I B E V Q T S M I Q N A L S T
S P F W N R L W S R T E V W S N A S G R G G G S
A E Z I V Z O V D S A O Z S I B Y Z N O D Y G Y
X A B L D W Z G Q U J X R D K Z S S E H E P O E
G K Z L D E Q T Q U J O S Z I F E I V S E S B K
O E Y I L K R I H E J D E B C D U G I R R X E R
D R U A X F X E T O S S O J K W T R U E H X D U
V S M M U A O N K U D O P Q A D O M S G U O A T
D P V S T Z E O P J F L R O M C F Y H O T G W Z
C Z V P C X Y R A G E A K E E R K U B R Z Y G W
X I D Y G I D M N O G T Y U T A K S H Q I E T T
U Y X F Q Z F Y J U S Z E S T E R B O P D X I P
R E N G A W S U N O H K Z R M W P D H N K M F O
```

Jud Wilson	Rod Carew	Hank Aaron
Turkey Stearnes	Wade Boggs	Tony Gwynn
Shoeless Joe Jackson	Roberto Clemente	Rogers Hornsby
Oscar Charleston	Derek Jeter	Babe Ruth
Honus Wagner	Ichiro Suzuki	Ted Williams
Edgar Martinez	Pete Rose	Tris Speaker
Paul Molitor	Willie Mays	Ty Cobb

ACES WHO RAKE

1. IEHSOH IONAHT _____

2. ONISDAM MRAENUBRG _____

3. BEBA TURH _____

4. BBO SBONIG _____

5. WANRRE SANHP _____

6. NOD DYDELARS _____

7. ZACK IKGENRE _____

8. KIME OANTPHM _____

9. DNO ONMBECWE _____

10. LARE LINSOW _____

11. JMI KATA _____

12. WES FRERELL _____

BASEBALL TRIVIA: _Shohei Ohtani is a two-way player drawing comparisons to Babe Ruth for his prowess on the mound and in the batter's box. With the designated hitter now being universal across both leagues, a new rule allows pitchers in the starting lineup as a hitter to remain in the game as the DH, even after being relieved on the mound._

The rule is unofficially referred to as "the Ohtani rule" because, let's face it, he's the only one it applies to!

BEST HOME RUN HITTERS BY POSITION

```
B H E M I K E S C H M I D T U A Z
Y G C S O L T W Z L T H R Q L L U
O T N U D B Y W I M G J P B Z J K
B Z O I U N X Y I L N W E F N S S
O G I C R R O K L E L R A Q P Z J
T T Y T R G E B K G T I W K B B M
N L U K R P U P Y P O T E J L N N
Y Y K Q I O I T U R A Y V M I W H
I N F A B R D J H K R E I C A H K
O V Z D L U O I B X L A G Q A Y B
I Z A A A L M U V J L B B N U A S
A E C E S D I X T A U K K C B X A
A O M S D W C E F V D A J E V Z H
T N E K F F E J J J A A R K M Y H
F A D Q F U P W Q R H U L H S Y H
W V B Z P Q N B O J T W D D K U P
E F A L Z M V N M H T J T B U B C
```

Babe Ruth	Cal Ripken Jr.
David Ortiz	Mike Schmidt
Hank Aaron	Jeff Kent
Willie Mays	Albert Pujols
Barry Bonds	Mike Piazza

HOME RUN SWAGGER

Across

3. This injured player pumping his arm as he rounds second base is an iconic World Series home run moment.

5. With a nickname like "Killer" and multiple home runs reaching over 500 feet, this played needed little "swagger" at the plate.

9. Fisk waves it _____ in Game 6 of the 1975 World Series.

10. Mets fans and teammates went nuts when this pitcher hit his first career home run. No swagger necessary when your nickname is "Big Sexy."

11. This player dramatically tossed his bat in the air after hitting a go-ahead home run in Game 5 of the 2015 ALDS.

Down

1. This player began calling his performance at the plate a "Laser Show," adding to his fierce persona.

2. Some people credit this Hall of Fame Yankees player as the "inventor" of the bat flip.

4. This player brought swagger to the plate with a backwards hat during multiple Home Run Derby appearances.

6. Rhys Hoskins took his time against this New York team when he set the record for longest home run trot.

7. Players from this team, including Freddie Freeman and Brian McCann, didn't take kindly to Carlos Gomez showboating a home run. The event led to the benches clearing.

8. In 2022, this team made headlines after hitting four back-to-back home runs in the first inning.

FAMOUS HOME RUN CALLS

1. "Bernie Williams goes back and it is...get out the rye bread and the mustard this time, Grandma! It is a grand salami. I don't believe it. My oh my! Edgar Martinez hits one off the tarp in dead center field!"

A. Dave Niehaus

2. "Fastball deep to right, this could be it! Way back there! Holy cow, he did it, Roger Maris. Holy cow, what a shot."

B. Jack Buck

3. "Smith corks one into right, down the line. It may go! Go crazy folks, go crazy! It's a home run and the Cardinals have won the game!"

C. Phil Rizzuto

4. "High fly ball into right field. She is gone! In a year that has been so improbable, the impossible has happened."

D. Vin Scully

5. "There's a drive to left-center field. That ball is going to be out of here. It's gone. It's 715! There's a new home run champion of all time and it's Henry Aaron!"

E. Tom Cheek

6. "A swing and a belt, left field, way back! Blue Jays win it! The Blue Jays are World Series Champions, as Joe Carter hits a three-run home run in the ninth inning. Touch 'em all Joe! You'll never hit a bigger home run in your life."

F. Milo Hamilton

TODAY'S BEST HOME RUN HITTERS

```
H C H R I S T I A N W A L K E R R A M M M V S Z X
X Y E V U O R U L O W I Y E S R N J S F K Q A S
U R T B E T G V K N M L C A K J O Y L O L H M I
L O Z F S H M I O U E I L T V O T L I R M E E X
U U U V P J K S E S F V K I P R X X U A R A N W
M H J Y V Y L Q C Z A L I E M E U F W U X K Z Z
T K Q U Z O T H T D S J T Y T R B G I S M M I Y
H D Z E T B W N O P U E O O L R N D D T N Q E Q
I N I T N A O R H Q A R V Y O E O D P I O N S C
N Y A M R E P S V L D K J Q E U R U O N T A E E
A M L B H E Y J O A U O I J A G Y V T R N A L R
T O E D R C U N N S S U F V Z R B J S I A M L A
H R D E Z A S A P E Q M Q L M I S F B L T I A M
O J Z A N O L D A E S F H Z M M K Z C E S T V L
I E N S H V N B L W G D K R A I B L N Y O C U M
E C O E A C R S E O Q D I X E D K I O A L H D G
H T G R L E A Q B R G B U W P A H L S K R H M I
O S E I U S X M T P T L Q J J L Q K H X A A A Y
H Z X Y Z T O I Y O R P U N N V R N H P C N D F
S X Y F E R D N C N B S U A R O S H N E N I A L
W B L Q I C H Z C U N S F J P P R O O O A G O W
I B R T X P M E A R R A R B O Q W A F G I E O C
P A L D L C R Z W X U B M U Y L Q L A A G R N M
G D N P C L O Y D F M Z D B P A S C I V C S Q W
```

Matt Olson	Mitch Haniger	Paul Goldschmidt
Yordan Alvarez	Byron Buxton	Mike Trout
Nelson Cruz	Austin Riley	Vladimir Guerrero Jr.
Manny Machado	Christian Walker	Shohei Ohtani
Jose Abreu	Giancarlo Stanton	Pete Alonso
Adam Duvall	Juan Soto	Kyle Schwarber
Salvador Perez	Albert Pujols	Aaron Judge

FOUR FOUR-BAGGERS IN A GAME

FOUR FOUR-BAGGERS IN A GAME

Across

5. This player's performance was part of an 18-16 slugfest between the Phillies and Cubs in 1976. His team clubbed nine total home runs.

7. This Braves player had a long-standing record for total bases in a game after he capped a four-homer night off with a double in 1954.

8. The most recent player to achieve the feat. He was traded to the D-Backs from the Tigers only a few months earlier. Every home run he hit was off a different pitcher.

9. Not only did this player club four homers in a single game, but he had 19 total bases, setting the record for the most ever. He had only five home runs during the 2002 season prior to the game.

12. 4 x 4 = 16 for this player, who had four at-bats, clubbed four home runs and totaled 16 bases in 1959 for the Indians.

14. The only player to have an inside-the-park home run in the mix. Actually, he had two for the Phillies in 1896.

15. This Reds second baseman hit four homers the same year as 8 Across, the second time two hitters achieved the feat in the same year.

16. Despite this player's multi-home run effort for six RBI, his team, the '86 Atlanta Braves, still lost the game.

18. Perhaps the most unlikely player in the club. He had only 71 home runs across 18 seasons, meaning he had more home runs than his season average during one game in 1894.

Down

1. A lesser-known White Sox player, he was the first American League hitter to join this prestigious club in 1948.

2. A Triple-Crown winner three years before, this Phillies player decimated the Pittsburgh Pirates on their home turf in 1936.

3. It took this player only five innings to reach this single-game home run club in 2002. He also went back-to-back twice in the same inning with Mariners teammate Bret Boone.

4. Similar to 11 Down, this future Hall of Famer also felt unwell prior to the game. Obviously, his performance didn't suffer during this 1961 game.

6. Every one of his home runs was a two-run shot. He had 18 total bases in the game, tying the record for second most. He shares a last name with a notable Founding Father.

10. This Cardinals player was in the second game of a doubleheader when he hit a grand slam, twin three-run homers and a two-run blast. His 12 RBIs tied a single game record.

11. After hitting his four dingers in 2003, this player surpassed 300 on his career and 40 on the season. He reportedly was feeling under the weather prior to the game. Go figure.

13. This household name among Dodgers fans had a total of 32 homers in 1950, meaning an eighth of his season achievement came in this one game.

17. A home run hitter whose efforts were largely overshadowed by Babe Ruth and the tragic illness that cut his career short. He had his four-bagger game against the Athletics during an exciting 20-13 game in 1932.

MOST HOME RUNS IN A SEASON

```
D R X D W K E N G R I F F E Y J R W T G Z Y O Y
X M Q I I Y X B S O H J M M V H B Z B E M Y B C
S C I Y J C V X A H L B R J J R T Q O Z P D Y H
W M F C S C T J F R N H W K W H R U W D G A U J
A Z B F Y X F E Y F R Q B C L F W R R Z L N S B
X Q O E R S N C R M C Y N Y M U W Z U E P P H U
S K U G U T N M V I Y A B Z C Q G L X Q B E D J
Z I T R O D I V A D W I P O M Z S R H X W A I P
H A X X W X Y V Q F M G V I N Y O Y I X I C B R
K N R E N I K H P L A R C S A D D O G E O M Q C E
C D S Q R I S U W R G K D M R I S E N F H Y I D
Q R H I D A R Q M Y E U E I K D O L J E B V J L
Y U A O R N C W T Y P I G U D R I V V I I S I E
S W N N E A T G M O L U R P G R A Q P M A I M I
U J K Z O W M A K L E L X E M Y U M R M U K T F
C O G O V S N R I Z U G F H S A R P M I D G H L
T N R L A T L W E S I O C F U N G Y E J Z H O I
V E E B L T Q I A G S M L F D H S A Z O A L M C
A S E E R K O Y W T O F Z B I O S H C U T R E E
U Y N N W P U D E K B R H B S W S J B P M W U C
U R B C L C R I X C X T A P A P F J B A M I F
R O E X J C V C O Q G A R H L R R H M P I C U B
Z O R W G O J C G S F U H L H D U C F X I W O H
O L G B E R K U A X G L U I S G O N Z A L E Z J
```

Andruw Jones

Cecil Fielder

Jim Thome

George Foster

Willie Mays

Mickey Mantle

Hack Wilson

David Ortiz

Ralph Kiner

Ken Griffey Jr

Alex Rodriguez

Luis Gonzalez

Ryan Howard

Hank Greenberg

Jimmie Foxx

Babe Ruth

Roger Maris

Sammy Sosa

Mark McGwire

Barry Bonds

THE 500 HOME RUN CLUB

1. RMAK MCWERIG

_____

2. FRNKA SIONORBN

_____

3. DEIED MYRRUA

_____

4. MLE OTT

_____

5. IIWLEL VCMECYO

_____

6. ANOMHR ELBLWRKIE

_____

7. GRIEGE ONCAJSK

_____

8. EIJMIM FOXX

_____

9. EIMK SDMHTIC

_____

10. UMGIEL RAABRCE

_____

11. NAFRK OSTAHM

_____

12. YGAR SDFHELIEF

_____

13. JIM OMHTE

_____

14. LEARAF EMPLIRAO

_____

THE 500 HOME RUN CLUB

15. MYCEKI ALMETN _____

16. SMYMA AOSS _____

17. ANYNM ZIEAMRR _____

18. NEK FGYEIRF JR _____

19. IDEED ATWESMH _____

20. TED ISLIWALM _____

21. DADVI IRZOT _____

22. INEER AKSNB _____

23. ELLIIW MAYS _____

24. TALRBE PJULSO _____

25. LAXE GRZIEODUR _____

26. BEAB HRTU _____

27. KHAN ONAAR _____

28. RRYBA OBSDN _____

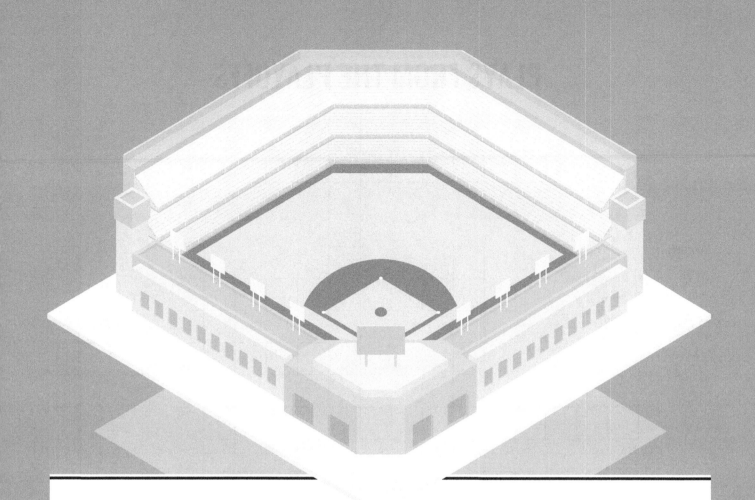

CHAPTER

PLAYOFF PUSH

As the weeks fall off the calendar, the season edges closer and closer to the playoffs. In the final month, every divisional race grows tighter and more intense. The season may be 162 games long, but it's always the last 30 that seem to matter most. Sometimes, it comes down to a final game to decide whose season will last a little longer.

Once the playoffs start, everything is on the line. One play can make the difference. The following activities are all about that now-or-nothing attitude that leads to glory or tragedy for a team's season.

PLAYS FROM THE PLAYOFFS

Across

2. This player snow-coned a would-be Scott Rolen home run in game 7 of the 2006 NLCS. Oh, and then threw it in to double-up a runner.

5. Bobby Thomson hit the famous "Shot Heard 'Round the World" to clinch the 1951 pennant off this Brooklyn Dodgers pitcher.

7. This player hit a walk-off homer in game 5 of the NLCS in 1985.

8. The Boston Red Sox beat this team after falling behind 3 games to none in the 2004 ALCS.

9. After a 16-inning saga in the 1986 NLCS, this team won the unofficially-titled "Greatest Game Ever Played" and went to the World Series.

11. A fan named Steve Bartman interfered with a play during the 2003 NLCS and potentially cost this team a chance to break a long-standing World Series drought.

12. In 1992, Francisco Cabrera was called to pinch hit for this team with the bases loaded. Cabrera had only had 10 at-bats in the regular season but delivered and helped push his team to the World Series.

13. The brother of 1 Down.

Down

1. The bane of the Red Sox and the boon (hint) of the Yankees in '03.

3. After winning a record-tying 116 games in the regular season, this team failed to punch a World Series ticket in 2001.

4. This pitcher topped off a Cy Young year in 2010 with an impressive postseason performance, including a no-hitter against the Reds.

6. This pitcher, known as "The Rocket," struck out 15 batters and allowed just one hit against the team that is the answer for 3 Down.

10. When 7 Across hit the walk-off homer in Game 5, it would have won the pennant the year earlier, but the series was changed from five games to _____.

ALCS MVPS

```
W H V K I R K G I B S O N S O K R E N O K L U A P Y N M N T O
S T Q P C D R S L L E W D I V A D Y E R E K L T C I B A L G O
Y L O R E N Z O C A I N T D R P C K Z I A L J T V T B T I F O
V A L C I D E S E S C O B A R S A T X E L A K V Z T N T E A Z
M W E K P E H F I D R C M R N Z M I T N X C J E M E E G X Y W
G W O T G C F N C E I G M O N P P A H E B M D W U A Z A A S E
G N T V S P X O L V D S S J Z N D Z I T K N Q U M G U R D X J
A L U V P B Q H R D B R X E K M A D E L A C X K Y Y F Z Z B P
Z R F O L G E O R G E B R E T T X R Z N L B E S C R N A V V O
O Z A U Y R D Z Z D A A S N B X Q O R X H I A B X A R H S D T
L Z L H S N Q D N S V H O I T K P E N V S F W S H G N V I A U
B N R H E J O E D L D T X O E S H N L M R T E E C S S C D R Z
H X I P S U H M A U L Y X F G O Y Q H A H D M M I C O F V D T
E E M W Y Y I N I I D T F U D L J X N D F X O R N N P J I R L
R M Q A E F A J M E V W S N D Q H K G E R F S P G D R Q U E O
Q D N K N D R A O G D E A E V N W A Y N E Y S M J I T E E D W
J A C T R E H X Y K N L R K L H T H V N K X I A A R R H B N Z
T I N O S H R L N Y R F I B I A E R L I C G R R C E O Z I A U
R T Y D S E R A M O L A O T R E B O R S I E G I K L C X N L R
E K E O Y L L Z Z X N V E L N S I C W E D C S A I L N T C R C
Z V J K L P P T W O R O K V J Y Q U C C D I I N E I A Y H E N
S T U U C W E T T E R R A B Y T R A M K O T U O B M L N A V O
Z V S T N U R T V E F A O T M R O E G E B S Q R R W O U W N S
A H S B L L P W T T N L Y C K O N G I R E U R I A E P X D I L
E A T N S A S Y U I E G X D B U P F D S K J A V D R O D R T E
Y B Z Q C P E P B G T E I D N H C H D L I D M E L D D G I S N
M L J T N L S S C R J T P A P A K J S E M I N R E N I B P U Q
D H L Q Q L K H O F I O E C R G R U E Y U V X A Y A C P S J D
A G V R X U N O N J G K W E G G N B W K G A E I J X A B M D O
O B E N U U Y D E N N E K M A D A N J W Y D N O R V L H B Y P
J D A V I D O R T I Z T R A W E T S E V A D D I L I P U F L N
```

Frank White	Dennis Eckersley	David Wells	Placido Polanco	Lorenzo Cain
Graig Nettles	Rickey Henderson	Orlando Hernandez	Josh Beckett	Alcides Escobar
Fred Lynn	Kirby Puckett	David Justice	Matt Garza	Andrew Miller
Mike Boddicker	Roberto Alomar	Andy Pettitte	CC Sabathia	Justin Verlander
Kirk Gibson	Dave Stewart	Adam Kennedy	Josh Hamilton	Jackie Bradley Jr.
George Brett	Orel Hershier	Mariano Rivera	Nelson Cruz	Jose Altuve
Marty Barrett	Bernie Williams	David Ortiz	Deimon Young	Randy Arozarena
Gary Gaetti	Marquis Grissom	Paul Konerko	Koji Uehara	Yordan Alvarez

NLCS MVPS

```
O R U L L E S N U O C G I A R C X V L H V K S Z O M M C A T P
R C G I W F Q O O M R F N V S Y Q N L N V D Q E V S R O K B Q
K F H R N F A X I F E U Q T Y T I R E L A U L P K D A L J M D
H Q S R W N X K P X G P E R D X T P G H T S U O E T R E D Y B
W V V W J I P E T S Q A V T O Y N G S R V B T L L M M L H M N E
Z M X H N S D A N I E L M U R P H Y A K W Y T Y D A W A G N N
M S P S C S T N B A S G H W O Z Y U T O O B W D R D V M Q J I
I E U O V C S A V H Y A M I B B L S S S H A D A G I A E U U T
D S T J Z K H E Y T E B H Z D E G L E R A K G J L S K L S S O
F T J U Q Y R M A L R Z D Z R H H T I M S E I Z Z O O S W T S
D P J S Z Y N Q W Z O G Z C I S C I L N N R M X W N E E E E A
A R Q T B G F E O O C R D V B D K U L W K J B P N B D Z H R N
V Q A I M K K O H W T C G M B J R M I D P R H Q G U D G T L T
I V A N R O D R I G U E Z G L S W A W T P S C Z N M I N T I I
D Y E T O R H Q Q O A N G X E Y H I W T S S M H M G E I A N A
F A H U Z E O R E L H E R S H I E R L O M J C Q N A P L M G G
R D O R T O L L I R T Y N N A M F Q R L H N U L L R E L Y H O
E I W N L M G Y W E D W U R B V Z Y D E C N S V X N R I R I X
E L I E O M O X E F T Q E N J P D W C A B L A U S E E H A T K
S L E R M G R N A R X H O Q O O X E M O R U A Y U R Z C G C X
E O K X S G J J Q J F T H I C I J A S A D E R R R K P S B H J
T H E D N M E Z O Z P F R T S T R R U T R Y L T K P H T G C E
L T N D H U O V E M W A E R S C A U A E E D B L H A Y R J O F
A T D T O U Q A A M S N T J O N P W V J H V M E P O D U E C F
W A R W J F B H H O M E P S D O Z E Y V C J E Y L O O C S K S
S M I M U R E W R U L V C Y H V D Y K C C S L G X L R T L J U
O U C K E K O E Q T P U M A K E P K Y T S H J D A J I T O Q P
Y G K I I I I N H A T Y N P K M J O N L E S T E R R W N E N A
O B V M D D I O Y A E B M I C H A E L W A C H A F C V A G R N
R A B W D N M A R R Z J M Z E D N A N R E H N A V I L E S E N
J D X E H P E O S A L B E R T P U J O L S G G G J Y K Y Y X R
```

Dusty Baker Jr	Mike Scott	Curt Schilling	Placido Polanco	Cody Ross	Chris Taylor
Willie Stargell	Jeffrey Leonard	Mike Devereaux	Ivan Rodriguez	David Freese	Justin Turner
Manny Trillo	Orel Hershier	Javy Lopez	Albert Pujols	Marco Scutaro	Cody Bellinger
Burt Hooton	Will Clark	Livan Hernandez	Roy Oswalt	Michael Wacha	Howie Kendrick
Darell Porter	Rob Dribble	Sterling Hitchcock	Jeff Supan	Madison Bumgarner	
Gary Matthews	Randy Myers	Eddie Perez	Matt Holliday	Daniel Murphy	Corey Seager
Steve Garvey	Steve Avery	Mike Hampton	Cole Hamels	Jon Lester	Eddie Rosario
Ozzie Smith	John Smoltz	Craig Counsell	Ryan Howard	Javier Baez	

MUST-WIN PLAYOFF GAMES

Across

7. A game 6 isn't normally a "must-win." However, knowing Mike Scott was prepared to pitch game 7 for the Astros in 1986, the Mets treated it like one. The game lasted this many innings, with the Mets securing their ticket to the World Series.

8. This young Marlins pitcher had a tough performance in the first game of the 2003 NLCS. He came back to shut out the Cubs in a must-win Game 5 and throw four scoreless innings in Game 7 to help his team enter the World Series.

9. This player was named the MVP of both the LCS and World Series during the 2011 postseason with the Cardinals. These achievements often overshadow the must-win Game 4 of the NLDS, where he had four RBIs.

10. In Game 7 of the 2003 ALCS, Aaron Boone hit a walk-off home run off Tim Wakefield. However, it was manager Grady Little's decision to stick with this pitcher in the eighth that hurt the Red Sox the most.

Down

1. A tiebreaker game between the Yankees and Red Sox helped decide the winner of the AL East in 1978. It was ultimately this Yankees player's home run that was the difference.

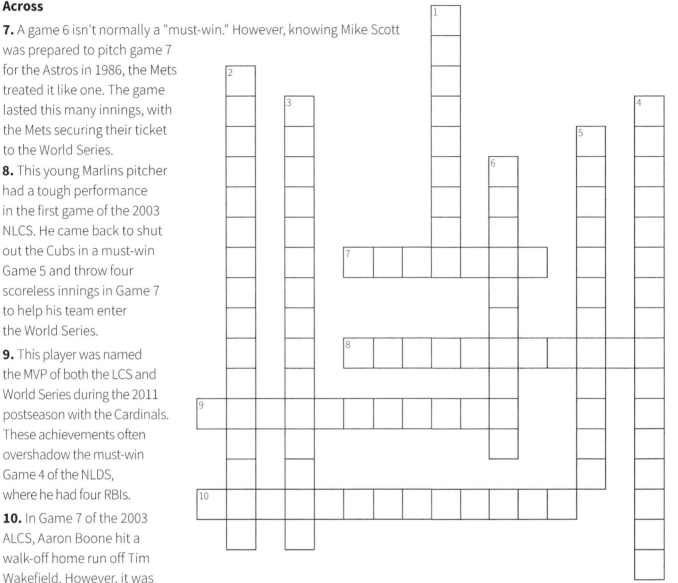

2. This Giants pitcher had one of the most legendary postseason performances. It started with a shutout performance during a winner-take-all Wild Card game against the Pirates.

3. This team played their first-ever playoff series against the Yankees in 1995. The ALDS went to five games with this team eventually winning on some late-inning, Game 5 heroics.

4. The Kansas City Royals played a 12-inning Wild Card game against this team. It was the longest elimination game to date.

5. This team played and won four consecutive must-win games against the Yankees in the 2004 ALCS after losing the first three games of the series.

6. "The Flip" play is one of this player's most iconic moments (in a long list of them). It preserved the Yankees one-run lead in a must-win game in the 2001 ALDS against the Athletics.

WHO SAID IT? PLAYOFF EDITION

1. "The throw misses the cut-off man, shoveled to the plate, out at the plate! Derek Jeter with one of the most unbelievable plays you will ever see by a shortstop."

A. Kenny Albert

2. "Ortiz into deep right field, back is Sheffield. We'll see you later tonight!"

B. Albert Pujols

3. "A manager has to convince his hitters that they have to get on base for the next guy and that no player can do it by himself. Sometimes that isn't easy. In the playoffs, you can get into trouble because everybody wants to be a hero."

C. Dave Niehaus

4. "It's not how you start the season, it's how you finish. If you wind up helping the team make the playoffs, that's what you play for. You don't play to put up your numbers, but to try to get a chance to make it to the World Series."

D. Joe Buck

5. "It's hard to win a pennant, but it's harder losing one."

E. Asdrubal Cabrera

6. "The 0-1 pitch on the way to Edgar Martinez. Swung on and lined down the left field line for a base hit... Here is Junior to third base. They're going to wave him in. The throw to the plate will be late! The Mariners are going to play for the American League Championship. I don't believe it! It just continues! My oh my!"

F. Chuck Tanner

7. "Bautista with a drive, deep left field. No doubt about it!"

G. Earl Weaver

8. "When you make the playoffs, it's like you've done your job for the team. I've got that moment in my mind all the time, and I want to be there again."

H. Thom Brennaman

POSTSEASON TRIVIA

1. In 1985, the League Championship Series changed from a best of five contest to best of seven.

TRUE	FALSE

2. The first team to come back from a 3-0 deficit in the LCS was the Red Sox in 2004 against the Yankees.

TRUE	FALSE

3. Sandy Koufax threw the only perfect game in postseason history.

TRUE	FALSE

4. Before 1969, there was no postseason except for the World Series.

TRUE	FALSE

5. Only the winning team can have a player be named the MVP of the series.

TRUE	FALSE

6. Due to a rainout, the Braves and Cardinals had to restart Game 1 of the NLCS instead of resuming play.

TRUE	FALSE

7. Derek Jeter's "The Flip" play saved the Yankees postseason dreams. It also saved this player after he overthrew the cut-off man.

A. Bernie Williams	**B.** Shane Spencer	**C.** Paul O'Neil	**D.** Jeremy Giambi

8. The current playoff structure allows how many teams to reach the postseason?

A. 16	**B.** 8	**C.** 4	**D.** 12

9. This player had one of the most iconic bat tosses after hitting a go-ahead 3-run home run in the 2015 ALDS.

A. Jose Bautista	**B.** Rougned Odor	**C.** Josh Donaldson	**D.** Kevin Pillar

10. From 1991 to 2005, this team made the playoffs every year, setting a postseason record.

A. New York Yankees	**B.** Oakland Athletics	**C.** Los Angeles Dodgers	**D.** Atlanta Braves

11. This team is the only one to never make it to the World Series.

A. San Diego Padres	**B.** Baltimore Orioles	**C.** Seattle Mariners	**D.** Washington Nationals

12. This team had the longest World Series drought. It spanned 107 years.

A. Boston Red Sox	**B.** Chicago Cubs	**C.** Philadelphia Phillies	**D.** Detroit Tigers

TOP PLAYOFF PITCHING PERFORMANCES

Across

2. Bob Gibson's 1968 World Series Game 1 performance holds the postseason record for the most of these in a game at 17.

5. Tom Glavine pitched eight innings and let up only one hit, winning the World Series for this team in 1995.

6. This Phillies pitcher threw a no-hitter in the 2010 NLDS against the Reds.

7. This player and 8 Across both have three postseason shutouts.

8. This player went "mad" in the 2014 postseason, pitching almost 53 complete innings and maintaining a 1.01 ERA.

9. You can't get any more perfect than this pitcher's performance in Game 5 of the 1956 World Series.

10. This current MLB player holds the record for most postseason strikeouts.

Down

1. This pitcher's bloody sock became the stuff of postseason legend in 2004.

3. This player has 57 World Series innings pitched and a 0.95 ERA, the lowest in history for a pitcher with at least five starts. He also has two shutouts and struck out more batters than innings played.

4. The best closer in baseball history repeatedly shined in the postseason.

POSTSEASON BUZZWORDS

```
A M C S O D C J F H J P T S D D O T S E B X N D
S U L T K H Z D A U C M Q L M H S A G U D D A Z
I S J D U A R C Z E I E V J Q O A D E R K F N
F T K H L F N T C E X A S P K Z T I V A S N R A
A W O G K X D V I V G Z V S O N V J C R X B G T
V I U T V V X E Y U Q D L T A I Q D R K P O U I
O N K O O K O N E A V Y C V S L L X M N D P Z O
R G U D L M R R P T M L D I I I C S X R G F F N
I A J H D B E I O W I A O V W E Z L E N M E H A
T M H H Y C D M V D N M F W T Y D L N X K T L
E E I Y O N E N C L S Y J J H T N Q Z A G F C L
T S U R Z S Z H E E D L C O V U K Y J R F G N E
O P D G C S E I R E S P I H S N O I P M A H C A
W Y N N A O F I G R T B Z Z O K Y X M U N Q Y G
I W D W H E E P E W O J H J J X T A X W A T P U
N X L A M S L K J V Q E S U C Y R M X G B E E E
I C Q O B F A N H Y O C V J G Q G M L B N J W D
L Z H W S E C N A G O W O J N H X C H N R O H R
L K H Z R B Z V L C A J Q C O S Y W A X I L I M
E J Y B J K B R O M I J H C T N G N D G C N M Y
D S E P I N F S E I Z P W W O T M F K D Q W W
H I T H C T U L C Q W D E A M Y B Y Y J L P N G
T K T U X S I M M P Q C C M E I E E L B V L W G
A Y Z Q G T Z E M C N I B B A R K Z R D Z T J P
```

Best Odds	National League
Underdog	American League
League Record	Home Field Advantage
October	Clutch
Fall Classic	Championship Series
Must Win Games	Division Series
Tiebreaker	

POSTSEASON UPSETS

Across

5. The 2016 World Series felt like it was going Cleveland's way after they tied the game in the eighth inning. However, this event gave the opposing Cubs a chance to regroup and ultimately win the World Series.

7. The 2019 Nationals were an underdog throughout the postseason but kept coming out on top in must-win games. They ultimately beat this team in the World Series, securing a franchise-first.

8. After falling behind three games to zero against the New York Yankees, few people expected this team to come back to win the 2004 ALCS.

9. The Athletics were clear favorites to win the 1990 World Series, but this team had other ideas, with several hitters batting above .500.

10. This pitcher was an untouchable force for the Cardinals in the 1960s. He was in peak form during the 1968 World Series but couldn't stop the Tigers from eventually winning in Game 7.

Down

1. In the 1979 World Series, the Orioles led the series 3-1 over this team. Ultimately, the birds would drop the next three games and lose the series, marking one of the best World Series comebacks in history.

2. The Mariners won a record-tying 116 games in 2001 but lost to this team in the postseason.

3. This Senators' pitcher was one of the greatest ever to play. He entered Game 7 of the 1925 World Series with three days of rest and a four-run lead. It seemed like a winning scenario, but the Pirates had other ideas and battered the pitcher for 15 hits.

4. A reporter labeled this team as "bottom feeders" prior to the start of the 2020 season. The team ended up making it the NLDS, upsetting the Cubs in the first round of the postseason.

6. The 1906 World Series saw the greatest difference of winning percentages in history. Some of this was due to this club's 116-win season.

PLAYOFF RIVALRIES

1. Yankees (2003 - 2004)　　　　　　　　　　**A.** Yankees

2. Rangers (2015 - 2016)　　　　　　　　　　**B.** Dodgers

3. Mariners (1995, 2001 - 2001)　　　　　　　**C.** Rays

4. Yankees (1996)　　　　　　　　　　　　　**D.** Braves

5. Yankees (1976 - 1978)　　　　　　　　　　**E.** Nationals

6. Phillies (2008 - 2009)　　　　　　　　　　**F.** Blue Jays

7. Dodgers (2020 - 2021)　　　　　　　　　　**G.** Astros

8. Red Sox (2007 - 2009)　　　　　　　　　　**H.** Red Sox

9. Rangers (2010 - 2011)　　　　　　　　　　**I.** Royals

10. Phillies (2007, 2009)　　　　　　　　　　**J.** Orioles

11. Dodgers (2016, 2019)　　　　　　　　　　**K.** Angels

12. Braves (2004 - 2005)　　　　　　　　　　**L.** Diamondbacks

13. Cardinals (2001 - 2002)　　　　　　　　　**M.** Rockies

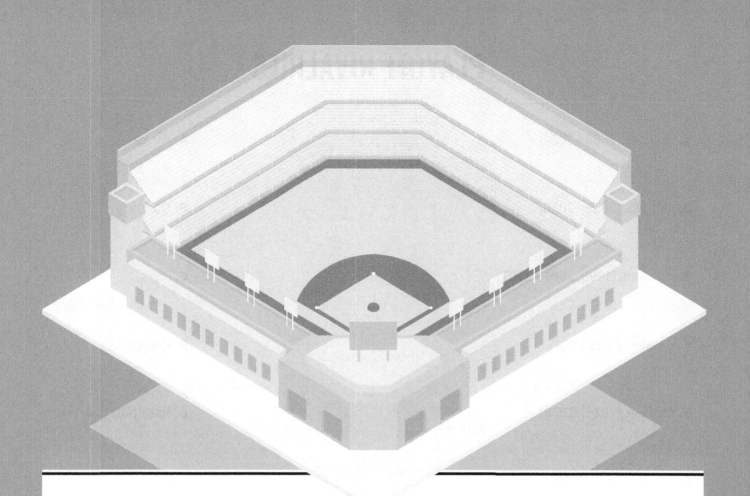

CHAPTER

THE WORLD SERIES

Ask a baseball player having a record-breaking season what it means to them, and they will tell you, it doesn't matter unless you win it all in The World Series. It is a chance to bring eternal glory to your team and the city you play for. There is nothing like it.

This chapter highlights the greatest moments in World Series history and the teams and players that made them possible.

WORLD SERIES REMATCH

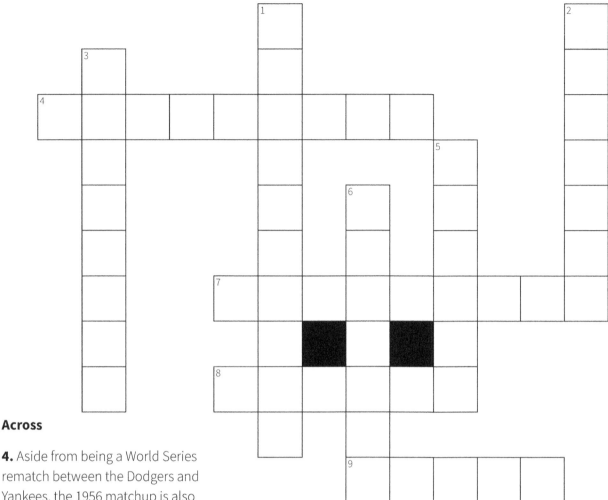

Across

4. Aside from being a World Series rematch between the Dodgers and Yankees, the 1956 matchup is also remembered for this player's perfect game performance in Game 5.

7. The Athletics and this team split back-to-back World Series titles in 1930 and 1931.

8. The Cubs seemed unbeatable in 1907 and 1908 when they easily won two titles from Ty Cobb and this team.

9. The Yankees and Braves split a rematch series in 1957 and 1958. Both contests lasted this many games.

Down

1. In 1942 and 1943, the Cardinals and Yankees played in back-to-back World Series, each winning a title. However, the lineups didn't include many stars because many players were involved in this global conflict.

2. Before the Giants moved to San Francisco, they routinely played in cross-town World Series contests with this team.

3. The 1990s saw Joe Torre's Yankees beating this manager's Atlanta Braves in two World Series contests.

5. The Yankees and this team played against one another for three consecutive World Series titles, including the last best-of-nine series using the old postseason format.

6. The Yankees and this NL team rematched several times in consecutive World Series events (77-78, 55-56, and 52-53).

MOST FRANCHISE WORLD SERIES TITLES

1. 27 World Series titles

A. Braves & Tigers

2. 11 World Series titles

B. Dodgers

3. 9 World Series titles

C. Pirates & Reds

4. 8 World Series titles

D. Giants

5. 7 World Series titles

E. Cardinals

6. 5 World Series titles

F. Yankees

7. 4 World Series titles

G. Red Sox & Athletics

BASEBALL TRIVIA: *The player with the most World Series rings is Yogi Berra at 10, meaning he was involved in 37% of the New York Yankees' titles. The rest of the list is several other Yankees players, including DiMaggio, Dickey, Rizzuto, Gehrig, Mantle, Ruth, etc.*

Eddie Collins has the most World Series rings for players who didn't play for the Yankees. For current players, look to Pablo Sandoval for World Series bling. He's got four rings currently.

WORLD SERIES GLORY

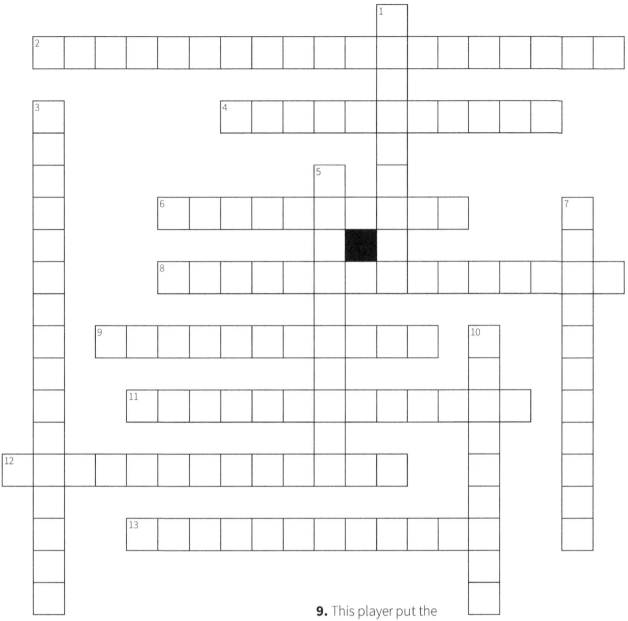

Across

2. This team became an MLB franchise in 1999. Two years later they beat the New York Yankees in the World Series.

4. This team won in 2016, ending over a century-long drought of World Series titles and putting to rest any "cursed" claims.

6. This injured Dodger hobbling to the plate and delivering a pinch-hit home run is World Series glory at its finest.

8. Don Larsen pitched the only perfect game in World Series (and postseason) history against this team.

9. This player put the Cardinals on his back in 2011, scoring big and multiple key moments.

11. This team, managed by Bobby Cox, made many World Series trips in the 90s, but only took home one victory in 1995.

12. This player hit one of the most famous World Series home runs in 1960 to give the Pittsburgh Pirates the walk-off win in Game 7.

13. This player provided extra-inning heroics to force a Game 7 and keep the Minnesota Twins' chances alive in 1991.

Down

1. This Cardinals pitcher recorded 17 strikeouts in Game 1 of the 1968 World Series.

3. After coming back from an 3-0 deficit against the New York Yankees in the ALCS, the 2004 Red Sox made quick work of this team, sweeping them in the World Series.

5. This future Hall of Fame player made the most famous over-the-shoulder catch in the 1954 World Series.

7. Everyone remembers Carlton Fisk waving a home run ball fair in the 1975 World Series, but this player hit the bigger home run earlier in the game to give the Red Sox the lead.

10. This Blue Jays player hit a walk-off home run to give his team their second World Series title in two years.

WHO SAID IT? WORLD SERIES EDITION

1. "My biggest moment was winning the World Series because everyone in my town was able to feel he was a world champion."

2. "When we played, World Series checks meant something. Now all they do is screw your taxes."

3. "You don't just accidentally show up in the World Series."

4. "The Dodgers win! Finally, the wait is over; the Dodgers are the champions of 2020. In a year like no other, when joy has been so hard to come by, Tonight, tears of joy, let 'em flow!"

5. "Red Sox fans have longed to hear it: the Boston Red Sox are World Champions."

6. "There's a drive into deep left field, look out now. That ball is going, going down. The World Series is over! Bill Mazeroski hits it over the left field fence for a home run and the Pirates win it 10-9 and win the World Series!"

7. "A swing and a belt, left field, way back! Blue Jays win it! The Blue Jays are World Series Champions, as Joe Carter hits a 3-run home run in the 9th inning touch 'em all Joe! You'll never hit a bigger home run in your life."

8. "I always got nervous the nights we played in the World Series. First pitch, I was nervous. Then after that, forget it; I'd start playing."

9. "They say the first World Series is the one you remember most. No, no, no. I guarantee you don't remember that one because the fantasy world you always dreamed about is suddenly real."

A. Don Drysdale

B. Yogi Berra

C. Johnny Bench

D. Joe Buck

E. Tom Cheek

F. Mel Allen

G. Derek Jeter

H. Sparky Anderson

I. Charley Steiner

WORLD SERIES DROUGHTS

Across

5. An expansion team added in 1969, they've been to the World Series twice, but are still waiting for a title win.

7. This team's 2005 World Series title snapped an 87-year drought.

9. Steve Bartman, a goat, and a black cat formed the foundation of a curse that kept this team from winning a World Series for 107 years.

10. This team is one of the oldest MLB teams and have won more World Series titles than the majority of teams. However, it's been over 40 years since their last.

12. The "Big Red Machine" was a dynastic force in the 1970s. This team hasn't done much since that era, rarely making it to the postseason.

13. The Rangers came within one strike of beating this team in 2011 and winning their first World Series.

Down

1. This team was dominant at the start of the 1990s, but that was almost 30 years ago. The closest attempt was back-to-back ALCS failures in 2015 - 2016.

2. This team came close to ending its 73-year drought in 2016.

3. This team is the only to never make it to the World Series.

4. It took this team 77 years to win a World Series, marking the fourth longest drought in baseball history.

6. Despite never winning an NL West divisional title, this team has been to the World Series, but is still looking for its first title.

8. Both the Giants and Astros had to wait this many years between World Series titles.

11. This team snapped a drought of 86 years and "reversed the curse" in 2004.

WORLD SERIES HISTORY

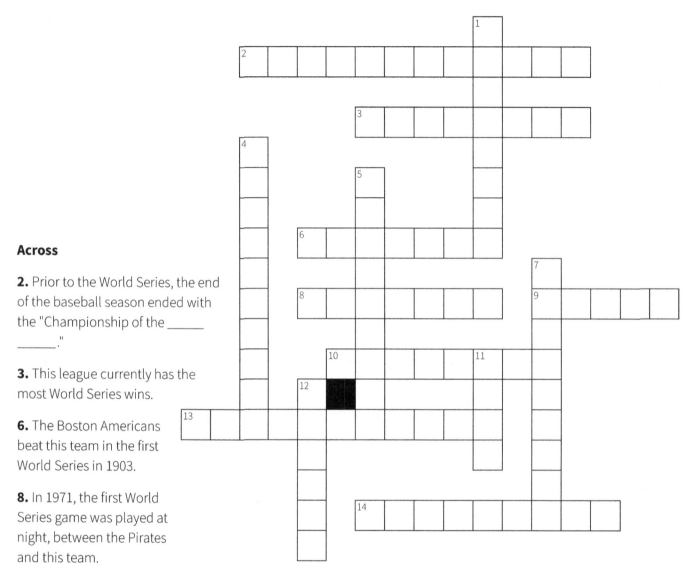

Across

2. Prior to the World Series, the end of the baseball season ended with the "Championship of the _____ _____."

3. This league currently has the most World Series wins.

6. The Boston Americans beat this team in the first World Series in 1903.

8. In 1971, the first World Series game was played at night, between the Pirates and this team.

9. There have been this many tie games in World Series history.

10. Teams from this league have won the past three World Series titles.

13. The New York Yankees hold the most World Series titles with this many.

14. This player threw the only perfect game in World Series history.

Down

1. This is the only team that has never made it to the World Series.

4. Game 3 of the 1989 World Series was postponed due to this event.

5. This team has the second-most World Series titles with 11.

7. Many people consider the 1905 World Series between the Giants and this team as the first "true" title after leagues came to an agreement on the proper format.

11. There have been four World Series contests to play a best-of-this series, instead of the usual seven-game format.

12. The 1994 World Series was cancelled because of this act by the players.

BAD TIMING BLUNDERS

Across

3. This player had a similar moment to 6 Down, failing to field a ground ball in the 2015 World Series that kept the Mets from securing the title.

5. Umpire Don Denkinger changed the course of the 1985 World Series after a bad call at first base kept this team alive in the ninth.

8. Babe Ruth wasn't known for his speed, which makes many wonder why he attempted to do this in the 1926 World Series. Spoiler: it didn't work out.

9. Lonnie Smith made this type of error when infielders tricked him into thinking a base hit was a routine ground ball, keeping the speedy player from scoring.

10. Through the first seven years of his career, this legendary closer made only one fielding error. The 2001 World Series was a bad time for his second one to occur, when he overthrew second base after a bunt play.

Down

1. Arguably the biggest World Series blunder of all, when eight players conspired to throw the World Series in what's known as this scandal.

2. Kevin Cash is the latest manager to come under fire for poor management of the pitching staff, particularly when he removed this player in Game 6 of the 2020 World Series.

4. This player made a boneheaded play when he forgot to touch the base after a walk-off hit by a teammate. The opposing team found the ball and stepped on the bag for the force out. Umpires deliberated and the game continued the next day. The player's team ended up losing.

6. This player became another chapter in the Boston Red Sox cursed history when he let a routine ground ball through his legs.

7. It doesn't get much worse than this. Willie Davis achieved an unfortunate World Series record when he made this many errors on two consecutive plays.

WORLD SERIES MVPS (2000 - PRESENT)

```
J E G Q Z V M N L E Y G P W Y X N B T H I B W C
D U Z A I R A T I U S T A M I K E D I H K X Y U
G S X T Z E N D S J O S H B E C K E T T G X B C
X K S U T L N E M I K E L O W E L L U A F S G C
D J Y G H O Y R R A R G D A V I D F R E E S E U
Q S L E L S R E W N D B R E G A E S Y E R O C R
B L S V A E A K U M U I O Z G E A X V C T D J T
X E R L O G M J M M M D S Z G Y L T U L G P V S
B M L B O R I E F D Z Q A O N K H H S E V F T C
D A V I D O R T I Z A I R G N E Y C C N Y E I H
L H H R Y J E E O K R V R T Z B B R O Y P R Y I
O E T Y E H Z R G E L J I E F E U S C H P L K L
B L G F Q G Y Y T H U K R D N M N M E R A I M L
B O N E W V N N E T C E E S E H U N G V Q J Z I
N C G Q L Z E I R C P Z H F O C S F O A E J R N
N N U C A R C O R R R O E J A T K D C R R F X G
G B O H R X Y P O P Z A Y X R B N S M Z X N J S
V X E A P G V D A N S D E A U A G A T W D C E Q
S Z G C L O A Z B C N E S B S D I J P E C B O R
C D B A J V U J T A U B G O E N E G P D I L A I
E T U B L W X Q R D U K L R E V Y Z I R E N U H
K S X A P M F Q G R T B B D O Y E X K F Y S H X
G A S E N D N M G Y A Z Y T C E H T F T T D S C
L H G C I T S G M P O E E A P M G O S B G J Y Y
```

Jorge Soler	Salvador Perez	Hideki Matsui	Josh Beckett
Corey Seager	Madison Bumgarner	Cole Hamels	Troy Glaus
Stephen Strasburg	David Ortiz	Mike Lowell	Curt Schilling
Steve Bearce	Pablo Sandoval	David Eckstein	Randy Johnson
George Springer	David Freese	Jermaine Dye	Derek Jeter
Ben Zobrist	Edgar Renteria	Manny Ramirez	

WORLD SERIES MVPS 1980 - 1999

Mike Schmidt
Steve Yeager
Pedro Guerrero
Ron Cey
Darrell Porter
Rick Dempsey
Alan Trammell
Bret Saberhagen
Ray Knight
Frank Viola
Orel Hershiser
Dave Stewart
Jose Rijo
Jack Morris
Pat Borders
Paul Molitor
Tom Glavine
John Wetteland
Livan Hernandez
Scoot Brosius
Mariano River

```
L L E M M A R T N A L A W J A P F G M R M T P Y
H N B V N D N P E Q M O I Z E C A E Y O C P E F
I Y R J L I T T A C L E M N T L C Q C Y Y S K U
A J E N S N R M Q U V M I H O R T A P I P K E A
Q X T Y C D D W P L L V O I O R A A R M A P I I
C Q S L O A X V R A A M V C U Y T Y E D V B C D
R Z A O O T G X M L T K O R M M T D K B G C S H
W L B R T R F T G M N B I L G H K P D G U U K
D K E Y B I A M J A K V O F I C G Y N P I H Q X
A D R Y R P O C R F O Z W R I T D U A E L G U C
R Y H O O T G F M R E V R D D O L L D B H H O
R B A U S J R H E E E D H T Z E P R E R U S T T
E F G D I A T S S V L N C H P U R J T O Z F D Y
L E E E U C F I T I H A Z Z G B J S T G L K I J
L J N F S K N W E R E N M K G K W L E U J X M Y
P J H S V M U L V O R R Y P B U J W E U H T
O Y Q W X O Q Q E N S E K Z Z S X Y N R P P C J
R T A E Y R S R Y A H H F D S D E Q R R B S M
T N J X S R X P E I I N R I D C Z V O E Z D E K
E C R F Y I G M A R S A G F N Y S Y J R A S K U
R P M F H S L C G A E V F O K V X L M O Q Z I E
A P W S X Y B N E M R I R Q X I D L J O G V M H
S H S W D A D H R W T L P T R A W E T S E V A D
T S H A H H J O S E R I J O X R V C D R G W Y P
```

MYSTERY WORLD SERIES CRYPTOGRAM

A	B	C	D	E	F	G	H	I	J	K	L	M	N	O	P	Q	R	S	T	U	V	W	X	Y	Z
				2		16												15							

T	H	E														E			T				H		
15	16	2		23	12	6	6	3	22	22	3	12	10	2	7		22		15	7	12	18	16	14

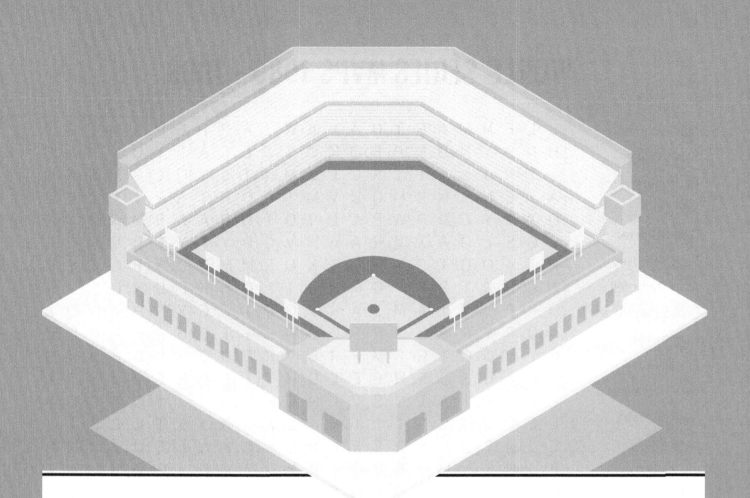

CHAPTER

THE HALL OF FAME

Every year, the Baseball Writers' Association of America (BBWAA) votes on past players, managers, broadcasters, and other people in the baseball world to join a special class of individuals. This class is known as the Hall of Fame. It is the highest honor in Major League Baseball and a mark of a truly exceptional career.

This chapter looks at the individuals deemed worthy enough by the baseball world to be permanently enshrined in bronze at the Baseball Hall of Fame in Cooperstown, New York.

MATCH THE CAREER RECORD TO THE PLAYER

1. Highest Career Batting Average (.366)

2. Most Career Singles

3. Most Career Doubles

4. Most Career Triples

5. Most Career Home Runs

6. Most Career RBIs

7. Highest Career OBP

8. Most Career Stolen Bases

9. Most Career Strikeouts (hitting)

10. Most Career Wins

11. Most Career Losses

12. Most Career Strikeouts (pitching)

13. Most Career Saves

14. Most No-hitters Thrown

15. Most Career Shutouts

16. Most Career Pickoffs

A. Ty Cobb

B. Sam Crawford

C. Mariano Rivera

D. Rickey Henderson

E. Cy Young

F. Ted Williams

G. Pete Rose

H. Walter Johnson

I. Steve Carlton

J. Barry Bonds

K. Nolan Ryan

L. Nolan Ryan

M. Hank Aaron

N. Cy Young

O. Tris Speaker

P. Reggie Jackson

NAME THE HALL OF FAME PLAYER

1. He's not the only one in his family to play professional baseball. He played for the Mariners, Reds, and White Sox. He played centerfield. Many people consider his swing the sweetest of a lefty.

_____

2. Best known as a member of the Montreal Expos, but his two World Series rings come from his time with the Yankees. He was inducted into the Hall of Fame in 2017.

_____

3. This pitcher made the move with the Dodgers from Brooklyn to LA. He has three Cy Young awards, despite ending his career when many people felt he was still in his prime. His nickname is The Left Arm of God.

_____

4. Primarily known as a Yankee, he also played for Cleveland, St. Louis, and Kansas City. In 1961, he broke the single season home run record with 61. His #9 is retired by the Yankees.

_____

5. The oldest person to play a MLB game (he was 59). He was born in Mobile, Alabama. Aside from many Negro League teams, he also played for Indians, Browns, and Athletics. He was known for his "hesitation pitch."

_____

6. He won the Rookie of the Year award in its inaugural season. In college, he was a four-sport varsity athlete. He helped the Brooklyn Dodgers secure a World Series title in 1955. His jersey number is retired by all teams in Major League Baseball.

_____

7. He orchestrated "The Flip" play against Oakland. He briefly spent time as part owner of the Miami Marlins. Him and his team secured five World Series titles. His nicknames include Mr. November and The Captain.

_____

8. Born in Georgia, he played primarily for the Detroit Tigers. He was a Triple Crown winner, secured 12 batting titles and won MVP honors. He's best remembered for his rough play style and base running.

_____

FUTURE HALL OF FAMERS

```
X M B G M C G R K B S D X R V U W A G Z M K U O
X Y U Y I U F G L H Y S T T E B E I K O O M M Y
T Q X G K D O N V V O U X U Q L J J V Y I H Y W
P U B S E D Y T D E Q T N J W A K W M W W S N X
O T L Z T M R N O P G K T T Y C G Y L O R Y O S
X O T L R H Y K N S L D H O L X G Q N A X L L
A B G T O D E W X G N U U A V R P S X D Y A A Z
R E O H U L K I A N H A Y J K Y H C I P F X N K
E V F G T N B J M V S T U Y N O E E J J X J A V
R M S M O R G E D B O C A J H O R O T G F P R X
B O G H H E G Z R N Y L T E R M R U J U D B E B
A W G I D Q J M K Z V M I E O Y B A I L F B N I
C X V R I H V E A K C O Z L T X B Q A X F T A L
L C C O E G R W S Z H R I U T K C B Q U V L D A
E M J R J S K S R T E N N N K K Y W Z G F C O G
U N B I H L K H A H A B U Y H T Y D K P X E A K
G J Y A L Q N N C S L O J U P T R E B L A P E J
I Y W N Y V I S K Y J S V L A H V U L E B O S Y
M D T G U H X J T S O P K D W X I C T Q I S T N
Z Q M S K A S X K E D J N M P D M J T P K B E O
E Q K Y M V H H P H O H T V K L U P E Z J R X N
N S V L A D I M I R G U E R R E R O J R C G X D
B G I X D H S B T A F H J G M W C W W E Q G N U
P V R X R E D N A L R E V N I T S U J J W V H B
```

Vladimir Guerrero Jr.	Nolan Arenado	Yadier Molina
Juan Soto	Justin Verlander	Miguel Cabrera
Joey Votto	Aaron Judge	Shohei Ohtani
Mookie Betts	Max Scherzer	Mike Trout
Clayton Kershaw	Jacob DeGrom	Albert Pujols

HALL OF FAME NICKNAMES

"You've never heard of the Sultan of Swat? The Titan of Terror? The Colossus of Cloud? The King of Crash, man!"

1. Schmidty

2. The Franchise

3. The Big Hurt

4. Teddy Ballgame & The Splendid Splinter

5. The Cyclone

6. The Wizard

7. Iron Man

8. Mugsy

9. Stretch & Big Mac

10. Big Six & The Christian Gentleman

11. The Commerce Comet

12. Mr. Tiger

13. Mr. Padre

14. Hammerin' Hank

15. Joltin' Joe

16. The Old Roman

17. The Kentucky Colonel

18. The Georgia Peach

19. The Iron Horse

20. The Flying Dutchman

A. Tom Seaver

B. Mickey Mantle

C. Earle Combs

D. Tony Gwynn

E. Hank Greenberg

F. Ted Williams

G. Cal Ripken Jr.

H. Lou Gehrig

I. Cy Young

J. Willie McCovey

K. Joe DiMaggio

L. Honus Wagner

M. Christy Mathewson

N. Ozzie Smith

O. Frank Thomas

P. Al Kaline

Q. Charlie Comiskey

R. John McGraw

S. Mike Schmidt

T. Ty Cobb

HALL OF FAME MANAGERS

```
I  B  J  K  C  P  L  S  E  I  N  H  C  E  K  C  M  L  L  I  B  F  J  J
M  V  U  C  C  K  C  U  O  J  O  Y  M  X  Y  T  L  F  R  C  D  K  O  N
O  A  B  C  M  A  N  O  T  S  L  A  T  L  A  W  E  I  D  X  A  Y  E  O
S  N  D  L  K  H  M  S  V  Y  D  V  V  P  O  V  D  H  O  O  F  R  M  S
N  M  T  R  F  Y  T  E  O  R  A  Q  D  A  L  L  O  P  E  Z  T  E  C  R
F  O  A  S  O  J  H  R  I  C  C  E  K  X  V  N  O  J  H  C  I  V  C  E
V  Y  L  I  N  S  W  A  O  N  M  L  L  O  I  B  C  H  L  Y  G  A  A  D
X  K  C  N  L  I  A  E  R  W  N  G  Q  C  K  J  I  F  V  P  E  E  R  N
G  Z  N  L  A  L  G  L  E  R  H  O  N  Y  R  I  E  P  T  L  F  W  T  A
L  J  L  G  N  H  I  G  Y  R  I  T  C  B  C  U  J  V  N  J  L  L  H  Y
Z  O  P  P  P  J  D  W  U  M  R  S  U  B  A  I  B  G  N  E  Y  R  Y  K
B  H  G  A  J  T  C  E  K  H  M  O  X  O  U  K  O  E  G  P  K  A  J  R
Z  N  S  B  F  O  R  X  N  C  R  O  T  B  S  Z  E  N  F  V  O  E  T  A
S  M  Z  S  V  N  I  D  V  L  I  E  T  E  R  Y  E  L  T  O  U  T  G  P
V  C  H  U  K  Y  R  R  S  B  V  D  L  E  O  T  L  B  E  N  S  X  K  S
W  G  J  R  L  L  P  K  Y  I  S  W  H  L  S  J  E  L  H  V  Q  T  Q  D
W  R  E  M  Q  A  Y  J  M  U  L  Y  O  Y  I  N  S  U  I  O  U  M  E  U
N  A  F  Q  X  R  X  F  B  A  E  C  E  J  Q  M  K  V  F  B  F  W  Y  R
W  W  W  I  J  U  B  G  X  T  T  S  W  S  K  L  N  S  N  D  F  E  D  V
C  E  B  P  P  S  M  Y  I  C  A  Q  Z  V  H  U  A  G  P  I  X  Q  Z  C
M  O  I  K  S  X  H  L  C  V  H  O  O  W  P  R  C  W  U  T  C  T  H
G  S  Z  L  H  A  W  D  B  X  G  V  I  I  X  O  F  Z  G  N  K  G  S
R  B  W  U  G  V  E  L  E  O  D  U  R  O  C  H  E  R  O  Y  G  V  E  K
M  C  G  N  O  S  N  I  B  O  R  T  R  E  B  L  I  W  M  Y  J  E  F  U
```

Connie Mack	Casey Stengel	Ned Hanlon	Dick Williams
John McGraw	Bucky Harris	Earl Weaver	Whitey Herzog
Wilbert Robinson	Al Lopez	Tommy Lasorda	Bobby Cox
Joe McCarthy	Rube Foster	Frank Selee	Tony La Russa
Bill McKechnie	Walt Alston	Sparky Anderson	Joe Torre
Miller Huggins	Leo Durocher	Billy Southworth	

HITTERS WITH 3,000 HITS

```
S D H U G E N R E Z Z C A L R I P K E N J R S P
Y W I A F S L O J U P T R E B L A T I T R R Y I
I P A K Y V D R H A N K A A R O N L T X E D A D
I K B D R A F A E L P A L M E I R O N K X P M A
Z H U E E R S K A A J P Y F S R R O A N Q N E V
G E I Z J B U Z O B A Z M T O V S E D A J N I E
Z T U P U Z O R G U M I Y B Q R P Q R P I W L W
K E S G B S E G L V G J E B E S V C I L E T L I
I L D X I C O M G U R R T D S U X H A A P T I N
J K N D O R O R E S T M N I E F O K N J D E W F
A U S U I L D L I O F E R V G N L H B O M R V I
W X O M I E C O C H H T S N U A X U E I H B T E
O F W T E A M L R Y C N U S H A A G L E X E T L
T I O H B Z E U E X I I W Y G T K T T B I G K D
G R G R B M R K R L E A N R O D C A R E W R R D
X L E G E M C T L R G L D N A X R W E F P O O E
A R O N I I N O S N A P A C Y E B P N E W E B R
A Y T U R B C F E A B Y L J N W O B T G O G I E
H E V L B E G R Q V Y N F A F K G E O U C P N K
R E O V I R R I J Q W L W N N H R Y S C X B Y J
O V R D D A O A A D G L R R Y O G E N G Y O O E
O F D G L O U C Z R U W C A S P P G A O Z T U T
U E X G U V K X K A C A N E C N A U O I T Y N E
G G T C A O G V P E P L A I S U M N A T S L T R
```

Pete Rose

Ty Cobb

Hank Aaron

Stan Musial

Tris Speaker

Derek Jeter

Honus Wagner

Carl Yastrzemski

Albert Pujols

Paul Molitor

Eddie Collins

Willie Mays

Eddie Murray

Nap Lajoie

Cal Ripken Jr

Adrian Beltre

George Brett

Paul Waner

Robin Yount

Tony Gwynn

Alex Rodriguez

Dave Winfield

Ichiro Suzuki

Miguel Cabrera

Craig Biggio

Rickey Henderson

Rod Carew

Lou Brock

Rafael Palmeiro

Cap Anson

Wade Boggs

Al Kaline

Roberto Clemente

PITCHERS WITH 300 WINS

```
O P Z N I Y I C L R Q Y G E A U N D S L Q R O Q
T H F O Y A F C K S G O F B N L O E N V L E N P
O O E S I C W P G V G E Y O U K J O L C P D Y Y
M J D W O R Y G G O E K H J I F T H H V O N Y V
S P D E M L O S W K U C P D H L C A E N K A T E
E M I H O Q K G M A L O N U R I R Q S W Z X R A
A J E T G D M I E E L I R A D L M U G N K E G E
V V P A I N T V W R C T C K E G T L A P M L G B
E M L M O O U Y L H C E E S E T A Y G W I A D W
R E A Y M Y E O O E V L R R O I R L K T V D Z D
M O N T O K C L Y E F A E N J N N Y V M E N A F
D Q K S C S S Z T Y D T U M A O R L G I B A T X
V L R I W Q E S W B C C Y L E R H L I I N L H M
H H M R N O K Y O L L T O G E N L N L H E E Y E
O M J H V V Y U G E O N E P R B S W S U P V S Y
K I R C M G R E G M A D D U X O K P Z O Y E M S
F T F A J N S V G L Z R N N O Y V C F O N L S K
V T G G P W G L N I O K V C X O X E Y F X C X L
D K J G S J A K T L S P S R X Z E V M Q H R K M
I S T K D V D P Y N H A P S N E R R A W J E S V
T Q J G I U Q A N O S N H O J Y D N A R V V K C
J Q A N A H G I H W O N O S K R A L C N H O J H
Q C E E J Y U B X N Q E P G N T R W O F T R B M
Q I C H T N N Y W Y L R A E F K C Q Q L K G Z T
```

Cy Young	Roger Clemens	Gaylord Perry
Walter Johnson	Tim Keefe	Tom Seaver
Grover Cleveland Alexander	Steve Carlton	Charles Radbourn
Christy Mathewson	John Clarkson	Mickey Welch
Pud Galvin	Eddie Plank	Tom Glavine
Warren Spahn	Nolan Ryan	Randy Johnson
Kid Nichols	Don Sutton	Early Wynn
Greg Maddux	Phil Niekro	Lefty Grove

LOU GEHRIG FAREWELL SPEECH FILL IN THE BLANKS

Lou Gehrig's Farewell Speech is iconic. Use the word bank to fill in the missing words.

"Fans, for the past two _____ you have been reading about the bad break I got. Yet today I consider myself the _____ man on the face of this _____. I have been in ballparks for _____ years and have never received anything but kindness and encouragement from you fans.

Look at these _____ men. Which of you wouldn't consider it the highlight of his career just to associate with them for even one day? Sure, I'm lucky. Who wouldn't consider it an _____ to have known Jacob Ruppert? Also, the builder of baseball's greatest _____, Ed Barrow? To have spent six years with that wonderful little fellow, Miller Huggins? Then to have spent the next nine years with that outstanding leader, that smart student of psychology, the best _____ in baseball today, Joe McCarthy? Sure, I'm lucky.

When the New York _____, a team you would give your right arm to beat, and vice versa, sends you a _____ — that's something. When everybody down to the _____ and those boys in white coats remember you with trophies — that's something. When you have a wonderful mother-in-law who takes sides with you in squabbles with her own _____ — that's something. When you have a father and a mother who work all their lives so you can have an _____ and build your body — it's a blessing. When you have a _____ who has been a tower of strength and shown more _____ than you dreamed existed — that's the finest I know.

So, I close in saying that I may have had a _____ break, but I have an awful lot to live for."

WORD BANK

WEEKS	GIFT	MANAGER	TOUGH
EDUCATION	LUCKIEST	GROUNDSKEEPERS	EMPIRE
WIFE	SEVENTEEN	COURAGE	GIANTS
EARTH	DAUGHTER	HONOR	GRAND

FIND THE COMMON THREAD

1. Gary Carter, Robin Yount, Ted Williams, and Ken Griffey Jr.

_____

2. George Brett, Johnny Bench, Hank Greenberg, and Jeff Bagwell.

_____

3. Yogi Berra, Roy Campanella, Ivan Rodriguez, and Johnny Bench.

_____

4. Ken Griffey Jr., Craig Biggio, Yogi Berra and Vladimir Guerrero.

_____

5. Curt Schilling, Randy Johnson, Luis Gonzales, and Craig Counsell.

_____

6. Lou Boudreau, Rickey Henderson, Kirby Puckett, and Jim Thome.

_____

7. Sandy Koufax, Pedro Martinez, Tom Glavine, and Eric Gagne.

_____

8. Pablo Sandoval, David Ortiz, Madison Bumgarner, and Salvador Perez.

_____

9. Pete Rose, Mickey Mantle, Willie Mays, and Robert Alomar.

_____

10. Omar Vizquel, Honus Wagner, Derek Jeter, and Cal Ripken Jr.

_____

FAMOUS IN THE BOOTH

```
N G Y A K L E A H C I M N E L L A L E M F V G C
Z B R H G B Q G D J E L G N I L R E T S N H O J
P T V E T W W A K L C J H K W L B S P E O S G
M Q G U B T E C N E Q D A V E N I E H A U S H R
A T T Y B N K C W R J B Q V M D G E Y M H H Z M
Y D B M O B E R J S F K V N T R M E R A A N I K
T A K Z U H A K E O C D A T T R A X X L R T M S
C M V C N H I G C V N M T K V J X N T G R N S I
Z J K U E Y D G Y I E M R V B X I Y U V Y S Y P
S K X I G O L D V L D Q I Q N O Q W D P K F M N
C B N T H R T L O A B A O L M Q B T Z G A D Y A
J R Q S J A E C U J Q Z I J L K Q U H O L B B I
E M S U N A Y V K C V W E P T E L H E Z A X P H
V U C V N R F X R Y S G V H Y C R Z B C S A Y I
R H A R R Y C A R A Y N T V T G B T J R K O E R
U U T E Q O I V X D C I I J W J F E V E O E M R
P X J L Z H K K O X C B V G R R X M B D O R F
S A T S O C B O B E G J M T C R E O S R K A Z B
G C O G L L U N M W Z Q M M Y F S B X A T D A F
O D O T U Z Z I R L I H P R I C X G M B R O I S
C O C O N C O Q Y R Q Q E L M T L Z U D X F H Y
F J O E M O R G A N K M O Q U N L K E E L I G O
G F H I I I G W Z Q Y V D D V Y P O V R D C U H
U X W C G G Q U A S F L R Q W K B Q O G J I Q V
```

Michael Kay	Mel Allen	Ernie Harwell
Jerry Coleman	Russ Hodges	Harry Caray
Jon Miller	Bob Costas	Phil Rizzuto
Jerry Remy	Harry Kalas	Red Barber
Joe Morgan	Dick Enberg	Bob Uecker
John Sterling	Tim McCarver	Vin Scully
Jack Buck	Dave Niehaus	

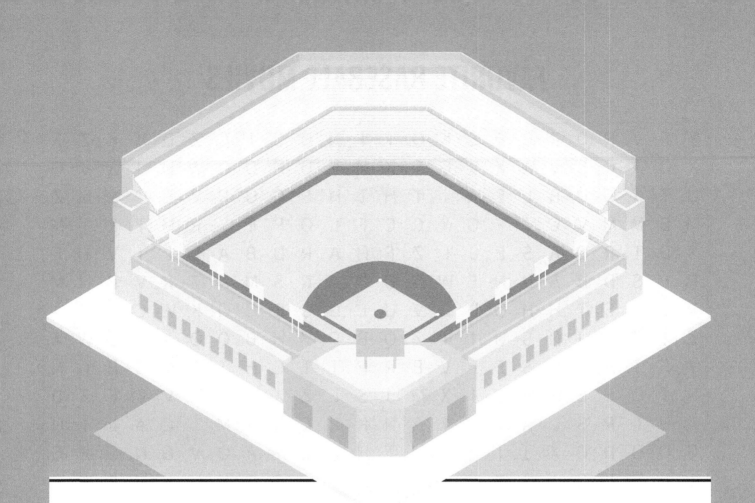

CHAPTER

10

OFFSEASON ODDITIES

Baseball is full of odd occurrences, wacky traditions, silly superstitions, and more. The offseason is always a perfect time to remember the more care-free and goofy side of the sport. After all, what else are we supposed to do while waiting for winter to end and spring and baseball to begin again?

In this chapter, you'll find puzzles and trivia about the fun and silly side of baseball, including some entertaining games you can use to pass the time during the offseason.

FAVORITE BASEBALL MOVIES

```
Y F V R D R B D S K O T I N D C I C Z D K K Z F
X O A C S V W X V G S K M E U K Q O W H J W V Q
U T R O U B L E W I T H T H E C U R V E Q S M Z
M B M M V C T F O X C C F L Q R E Y R M T E I M
S D T R O A S E J L Z F H A R D B A L L I V L F
R L S D B A D N E W S B E A R S M H Z R V B N M
V E B S T H H O U B V U L G G B C O K W C R E A
Z I P M J N S U I I Z Q B P V H B Q O A A O W A
Y F T A I M S F E V E R P I T C H T A M G B L N
N T O E E W M O I X M J S L Z X A A R V E E Z D
F U L R S D A M N Y A N K E E S V M T C A L I U
G O D D Q X J I H E M B T H P C Y A O V G N Z C
I E N F S I O Y C U S A T Y E F C N U K U E W R
V H A O W X R Y I P H Z H I Z V W E L E H I B Y
H T S D C Y L M K V P J K R H E O Y K Z F G W H
I N E L O C E L Z B S O I U U F X B I J M H F M
V I H E B Q A O N V O B M B T D X A X A J T C C
C S T I B Q G I Y R M A G H W Y L L V J I M R K
N L S F C W U Q E A Q F E W A T L L W J C E Y J
T E I D Z E E H H U M I O L N Q M A U E M N I A
O G R A Y Y T R M B R H O M Y H Z L T B C O T M
T N A R Y C H A S O O Z L Z U A C U V L I U P E
J A L G L T O D W K L U L G U J Y V Z J K T X T
B M D U A S Y N U I Z L X H H H S R K K G K K Y
```

Damn Yankees	*A League of Their Own*	*Moneyball*
Angels in the Outfield	*Major League*	*Bull Durham*
Cobb	*The Sandlot*	*Trouble with the Curve*
Bad News Bears	*The Rookie*	*Field of Dreams*
Eight Men Out	*Hardball*	*Fever Pitch*

BASEBALL IN MUSIC

```
K Q Y I E C V R G L O O V D G I Y P N X X X Y X W
T J L E D K K M T N X Y G L E Q M P V S X S U X
S M Z U M E W G D H O L L A V J E U M D J C Z Q
M L D F C U W C F Y B S Y G W Y Y T O T I K S C
S E X X W E J K Y G C A L J D Q X Q P F G B B H
J U I K I K G D T D L P V L B B X J C P I R N D
Q O S S Z Z Q G V T Z L V I A A G J H I V U Y L
N P L K S I Z Q C Z V P A X K B F A S D Q J B E
Q N A T N E B K N Q N V D B B X E O K L T U N I
E Q T E I U T I Y H U L M E E U I S G D R X F
E W S L N G D L O E P N T O S P D A K T C Q R
L V F E R H J I P I X I I V B T A A L B U U M E
C R R N T M R O F W L H N J Z W T B I O D P P T
W Z K G Y R B T E O L V Y E H Y A S N F F S N N
H H A O E D H U R D B E Q P N V P N A I W X C E
W M H H G G R A Q X I X Q F O E Z T J B K B N C
E M C B I N C Z U X S M W G V H R Q Q T L B G
Y O O R F T P J S I T N A H F P P I K L C V A A
W L Y F E W A K L C S Q B G D U M W U H Z F U T
S T A E S P A E H C T D V G G Z D X B X Y O A E
R N W M E H G J X G L P T U B I Z U K E C U Q X
B S S Y A D Y R O L G I O R C M O L C Z B R E W
B R Q A P W J R R D O D G Y Q Y Z W P Z D C N G
B X I R Y O O R Z G D Q M V I F E E O X P L U T
```

Say Hey	Sweet Caroline
Centerfield	Tessie
My Oh My	Glory Days
Cheap Seats	Joltin' Joe DiMaggio
Night Game	Talkin' Baseball
Right Field	Baseball Song

HARMON KILLEBREW CELEBRITY NAME GAME

Entertaining a large crowd and need a baseball-themed party game? Try Harmon Killebrew. This is a celebrity name game you can play with a large group or just a few friends.

Gameplay: Each game starts with the player whose birthday is closest to Harmon Killebrew's (June 29). That player says the name of any celebrity. Play then proceeds clockwise to start. The next player must name a new celebrity whose first name starts with the first letter of the previous celebrity's last name.

For example, if a player says the name "Jackie **R**obinson," then the next player's celebrity must start with the letter "R." They might say, "Roger **M**aris," giving the next person the letter "M" to start with.

The object of the game is to reach the name "Harmon Killebrew." The player whose turn is next is now out of the game. If you don't want to exclude anyone, you can play cooperatively, where the object is to reach "Harmon Killebrew" in as few turns as possible.

Alternatively, you can play an adult variation involving alcoholic drinks. In this version, the person after "Harmon Killebrew" is said must do like the name says and kill their brew. If you're using these rules, remember to always drink responsibly.

After "Harmon Killebrew" is said, the next person starts a new round with a celebrity name of their choice.

Double Letter Names: When the first and last name of a celebrity starts with the same letters, the turn order is reversed. Here's an example:

Player 1: "Roger Maris"
Player 2: "Mickey Mantle"
<Play order reverses back to Player 1>
Player 1: "Mike Mussina"
<Play order reverses again to Player 2>
Player 2: "Mitch Haniger"
Player 3: "Harmon Killebrew!"

What names are allowed? It's entirely up to you what names you allow in your game of Harmon Killebrew. You can play only with baseball players or open the game up to include any celebrity name the group agrees on. You can also include fictional characters (Harry Potter, Mickey Mouse, etc.)

BASEBALL TRADES THAT ACTUALLY HAPPENED

1. Lefty Grove is a Hall of Fame pitcher with 300 wins and a lifetime ERA just around 3.00. You might be surprised to know a former team traded him to the Orioles for a whopping $3,500 used to repair this. The Orioles would later sell Grove to the Athletics for just over $100,000. Not a bad investment.

| **A.** An outfield fence | **B.** A flooded dugout | **C.** The team bus | **D.** The pitcher's mound |

2. Dodgers catcher Cliff Dapper was traded in 1948 for a broadcaster instead of another player. Who was the broadcaster?

| **A.** Vin Scully | **B.** Mel Allen | **C.** Ernie Harwell | **D.** Red Barber |

3. Sometimes teams make a trade for "a player to be named later." In John McDonald's case, the player to be named later was himself. In other words, McDonald had the bizarre experience of being traded for himself by this team.

| **A.** Cincinnati Reds | **B.** Chicago White Sox | **C.** Seattle Mariners | **D.** Toronto Blue Jays |

4. Johnny Jones didn't get a chance to play much baseball. However, he does have a weird place in baseball history. He was traded for this food item that was later served at an annual dinner for the Southern Writer's Association.

| **A.** A homemade pie | **B.** A 25-pound turkey | **C.** A crate of wine | **D.** A roasted pig |

5. Cy Young is another Hall of Fame player involved in a bizarre trade. He was sent to Cleveland for $300 and a new one of these.

| **A.** A car | **B.** A suit | **C.** A watch | **D.** An autograph |

6. This team did some clever dealing when they traded Tris Speaker in return for using a stadium for Spring Training. They then re-acquired Speaker as his career started heating up, effectively restarting his MLB career.

| **A.** Boston Red Americans / Red Sox | **B.** Washington Senators | **C.** Detroit Tigers | **D.** Pittsburgh Pirates |

KICKED OUT OF BASEBALL

Across

3. Eight players from this team were banned in 1921 for working with gamblers to throw the 1919 World Series.

5. Inducted into the Hall of Fame in 2011 as a player, his former team cut ties with him due to sexual harassment claims from a staffer.

6. This player was banned in 1980 after a customs search in Toronto turned up a number of controlled substances. He was later reinstated and eventually voted to the Hall of Fame in 1991.

7. This baseball commissioner died eight days after banning 10 Down.

11. This Yankees owner was banned for working with unscrupulous individuals in an attempt to dig up dirt on one of his own players.

Down

1. The team that cut ties with 5 Across.

2. The only woman to be banned by MLB. The former owner of the Cincinnati Reds was banned for repeatedly making slurs against multiple groups.

4. The player 11 Across was trying to discredit.

8. Jack O'Connor and Harry Howell were both banned in 1910 for trying to fix the outcome of a batting title race between Nap Lajoie and this Tigers Hall of Famer.

9. In a weird twist, Commissioner Kuhn banned Willie Mays and Mickey Mantle after they were hired by this type of establishment in Atlantic City as greeters and autograph signers.

10. This record-holder for most hits in a career was banned in 1989 for betting on his team as a manager.

YOGI-ISMS FILL IN THE BLANKS

Yogi Berra was full of great sayings and advice. Use the word bank to fill in the missing words.

Yogi-ism #1: "It ain't over 'til it's _____."

Yogi-ism #2: "I can't _____ and hit at the same time."

Yogi-ism #3: "All pitchers are _____ or crybabies."

Yogi-ism #4: "Always go to other people's _____ . Otherwise, they won't come to yours."

Yogi-ism #5: " _____ is the most important thing in the world, but baseball is pretty good, too."

Yogi-ism #6: "If the world were _____ , it wouldn't be."

Yogi-ism #7: "Baseball is 90 percent _____ . The other half is physical."

Yogi-ism #8: (On Sandy Koufax) "I can see how he won 25 games. What I don't understand is how he lost _____."

WORD BANK

Yogi-ism #9: "In baseball, you don't know _____."

Yogi-ism #10: "It's _____ all over again."

Yogi-ism #11: "A _____ ain't worth a dime anymore."

Yogi-ism #12: "When you come to a _____ in the road, take it."

Yogi-ism #13: "He hits from both sides of the plate. He's _____."

Yogi-ism #14: "The _____ ain't what it used to be."

Yogi-ism #15: "You can _____ a lot by watching."

PERFECT
OBSERVE
FUNERALS
AMPHIBIOUS
FIVE
OVER
NOTHING
FORK
LIARS
DEJA VU
THINK
NICKEL
MENTAL
FUTURE
LOVE

CELEBRITY BASEBALL FANS

```
E K B L I H G C M Q M D G S T E P H E N K I N G
L E L Q W E W N G M F C H L L E R R E F L L I W
S A I C C A H V A F Z Y T G M M M X W Z H R R J L
R I B H S M B H R Y S N U E A I I B M R C N A Z
S F O G O J N A A X T A G O R L Z Y B W W Q T G
K C V A J O R R R H E X X T Y A Q C R K W J D F
U U Q A J Z R R F A D R F M H K N K A A E N S W
I M G D A U O B Y E C I K Q A U D M L N X A L P
T M T P M H D O O E A K M F R N D E N Z R H O O
K Q N L A Y S A E L F U O P T I U A X A P G G T
H C L W I L S U I Y K A D B Q S F L H E A B G U
H I Z W N N W C B R D W N B A I Q J M N O S P N
B U Y G F X E M D W U E I I S M E O L V Y V S E
T D A P U C H D F W E L S C T S A N O H I T R D
U P J C O R U U W D L G H C S M S P H J A Q B X
N N V O T R T J S N Y E R I H R R E C K A I U T
V H Z R L N K W Y F R U C O O A E O K K P F P U
V E Z U J J E E D N E A W Y E Z N O V A K P V Z
R A A N Z F K Z G Y P O R X D G Q E L C L Z A P
T P W G A L Y S S A M I L A N O H E L A V C K Q
V C D A F W M J R Q S J E R R Y S E I N F E L D
V A P Y T X Q K I L Q A N I C K S W A R D S O N
R Y F E X A E K Q R N A M R E T T E L D I V A D
T D G E M R C Z Z T K A T E U P T O N W K W X X
```

Alice Cooper	Mary Hart	Kate Upton
Alyssa Milano	Tina Fey	Barack Obama
Jenna Fischer	Jay Z	Mila Kunis
Zooey Deschanel	Jerry Seinfeld	David Letterman
Bill Nye	Nick Swardson	Bill Murray
George W Bush	Will Ferrell	Sarah Jessica Parker
Jon Hamm	Paul Rudd	Stephen King

BASEBALL MEMORABILIA YOU WISH YOU HAD

Across

2. The most expensive baseball memorabilia tends to come from old players and Hall of Famers. Yet, a rookie card for this current MLB player sold for almost $4 million.

6. Just about anything Babe Ruth touched is worth a high price. One of the most interesting pieces of memorabilia is his contract when he was traded from this team to the Yankees.

8. Joe DiMaggio and this Hollywood star were briefly married and once signed a baseball together that fetched nearly $200,000.

9. A Babe Ruth baseball sold for $700,000 because it was the first home run ball from this mid-summer baseball event.

Down

1. The baseball from this player's "Shot Heard 'Round the World" home run disappeared after the event. Estimates put its value at $3 million minimum.

3. A collector paid $3 million for this player's 70th home run ball from his 1998 season.

4. A baseball card featuring this player recently sold for $12.6 million.

5. Price tags for this player's T206 baseball card from 1909 regularly enter the millions, even as high as $6.6 million.

7. At the very first Hall of Fame induction ceremony, 11 members, including Ruth, Cobb, Wagner, and others, signed this item, which sold for $623,000.

AWARDS, TROPHIES, AND ACCOLADES

```
K C O M E B A C K P L A Y E R O F T H E Y E A R
D F J P X R L R L P M F A P R I K R Y F Y G U I
R H E F A M E O Q M I I E T V G P W C H D S Z R
A A K R D M Y Y G Q X S V W U X B I P E P T E F
W N F G A A Z R A X U H X U Z S X O Z N J L T Z
A K G E U E E Q O L W C Z S U U R H M P I P K G
L A O Q I T Y B R O P K X M H T L N V E R Q X W
A A K G D B S E S I K E Q U S G R M V X E I W B
I R U O F L H D H T K I L R N B E E Y C V I O Q
R O A R Z M R C B T K R E B V M R Y Y F O Z R F
O N W C G L Z Z Q X F N M O A O T L X Z L H L H
M A C R L L O B C O O O R G F U B C X D G T D P
E W Z Q G A D K R I E E R T O T L B O R D K S C
M A V S X N D O S T G A H E R N H A E V L J E Y
G R A E A N H S L G T E E S G U T E V C O V R Y
I D L N F S I I U S Y K V N P A W M Y T G Q I O
R T M W E M O L L E G R A J T D N Q N E S L E U
H O G Z M G S L A I S R J D N X B A L K A O S N
E L J O K A R N E L D E I N S I S M D R R M G
G Q C P E T E M W W X I A Y O Z J Y S L L O V A
U J E V D R A W A Z E N I T R A M R A G D E P W
O R L X W A R R E N C G I L E S T R O P H Y X A
L I Y H P O R T E G D I R R A H M A I L L I W R
S I D R A W A E T N E M E L C O T R E B O R T D
```

Warren C Giles Trophy	World Series MVP	Manager of the Year
William Harridge Trophy	Comeback Player of the Year	Rookie of the Year
Edgar Martinez Award	Hank Aaron Award	Cy Young Award
Reliever of the Year	Silver Slugger	Lou Gehrig Memorial Award
All-Star Game MVP	All-MLB Team	Most Valuable Player
Roberto Clemente Award	Gold Glove	Commissioner's Trophy

117 CHAPTER 10 - **OFFSEASON ODDITIES** | THE ULTIMATE BASEBALL ACTIVITY BOOK

MULTI-SPORT PLAYERS

Across

2. Danny Ainge has two NBA championships under his belt. However, he also has an MLB home run on his resume from when he was a prospect for this team.

6. Dave Winfield had an MLB career that spanned over 20 years and six different teams. He's still involved in MLB player operations. Once upon a time, he was drafted by this NFL team.

8. The athlete from the 4-Down clue spent his short baseball career playing for this MLB organization.

9. Russell Wilson is known as an NFL quarterback. He also spent time with three different MLB teams, starting with being drafted by this one.

10. This player performed at a high level in the NFL and MLB. He was even an NFL Pro Bowler and MLB All Star within a year apart.

Down

1. Nicknamed "Prime Time," this athlete played for four different MLB teams and four different NFL teams.

3. Cal Hubbard is an interesting case. He was an NFL player with the status to make it to the Pro Football Hall of Fame. Later, he took on the role of this in the baseball world and also became inducted into the Baseball Hall of Fame.

4. Commonly referred to as the Greatest of all Time in basketball, this NBA super-giant spent some time trying baseball.

5. He played in the NFL, became a broadcaster, and then tried his chances at baseball, spending time in the New York Mets organization.

7. Jackie Robinson is known for his baseball heroics and shattering the color barrier, but he was a multi-sport athlete, reaching varsity status in this many sports during college.

WEIRD BASEBALL NAMES

```
K H J I G B O Y W M A R L O N B Y R D R D B U I
D G Y A R O K C W S C Y B P K E F G A P L S U L
F W W W O L K O C R A P Z M D D P T K H O F F U
S L M I L T O N B R A D L E Y D T Z Y V O S O T
E I J P J S X C A X C X S B G Q J I E V J A R B
N L J B K E V R M Z Y O O K O U I W V U I F P U
I B O F W E G Z Y G F O C U W P E Q K H J B R T
H B Y Z M Y H A R Y F N M O A A D X C P Q A G T
S M Z O O A G Q S B O S K Z C J H C C V M V C E
R O E P V O A D O S A F P N G R A N H J P O M R
O C B B G E N L E O O Z Q Q M I A E W S Y S C A
Z T F K Y Q S B X H G G Z Q A K N S N K Q Y N U
A I D G C E F P U A S V E L X A K W P P C W K P
R T C S R G O J A D Z H A S T W I C M X S I H D
U L D D S H F O T A W T Q N O L Y G I P X C H I
A L N H C S Z P I I L E A K L O E P I U E M B C
G A H C M E K C R A E S I R I Q G M P Z X X K K
R B I S Z Q S Q S T S E H S T W A P V U Y Z K E
A N J C K N N D O O H Y G Z E J A Y F E A D D R
C O Y C K B O T L A M V K V O R H Y G T S R W S
E N Y N T R J R Y E R E T N U H H S I F T A C O
C N U W R H A J S A G S F F H T R G E V G M A N
S A W A Z C I L A L A L B U R Q U E R Q U E L T
J C J L T X P Y I Q U H R Z F N G X G O P M I E
```

Cannonball Titcomb	Buttercup Dickerson	Will Rhymes
Chicken Hawks	Catfish Hunter	Marlon Byrd
Boof Bonser	Carlos Santana	Jarrod Saltalamacchia
Razor Shines	Al Alburquerque	Milton Bradley
Bud Weiser	Coco Crisp	Goose Gossage

CONCLUSION

You've made it to the end of this baseball puzzle book. You've smashed a home run on every crossword, word search, and trivia page. You're a true baseball fanatic! We hope you learned something new about America's pastime while enjoying this crossword puzzle book. There's so much to know about this great sport!

Looking for more puzzles? Don't forget to check out our other puzzle books for everyone.

SOLUTIONS

WAITING FOR BASEBALL TO RETURN (PAGE 3)

THE FUNDAMENTALS (PAGE 6)

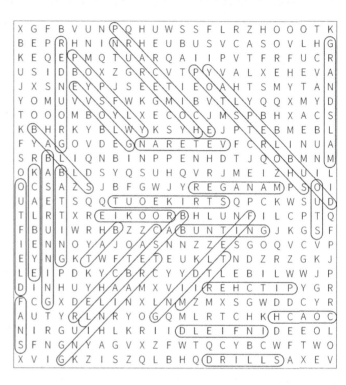

A NEW SEASON (PAGE 5)

BACK TO BASICS (PAGE 7)

SOLUTIONS

MATCH THE TEAMS TO THE SPRING TRAINING LEAGUES (PAGE 8)

Cactus League: Chicago Cubs, Texas Rangers San Diego Padres, Colorado Rockies, Seattle Mariners, Kansas City Royals, Oakland Athletics, Arizona Diamondbacks, Los Angeles Dodgers, Milwaukee Brewers

Grapefruit League: Washington Nationals, Houston Astros, Miami Marlins, New York Yankees, Pittsburgh Pirates, Toronto Blue Jays, Baltimore Orioles, Boston Red Sox, Tampa Bay Rays, Atlanta Braves

GRAPEFRUIT LEAGUE TEAM LOCATIONS (PAGE 10)

1. Blue Jays **2.** Phillies **3.** Yankees
4. Tigers **5.** Pirates **6.** Orioles
7. Braves **8.** Rays **9.** Twins
10. Red Sox **11.** Mets **12.** Cardinals / Marlins
13. Astros / Nationals

CACTUS LEAGUE TEAM LOCATIONS (PAGE 10)

1. Royals / Rangers **2.** Mariners / Padres
3. White Sox / Dodgers **4.** Reds / Cleveland
5. Brewers **6.** Angels
7. Giants **8.** Diamondbacks / Rockies
9. Cubs **10.** Athletics

SPRING TRAINING STADIUM UNSCRAMBLE (PAGE 9)

1. George M Steinbrenner Field
2. JetBlue Park
3. Clover Park
4. Charlotte Sports Park
5. TD Ballpark
6. Roger Dean Chevrolet Stadium
7. Goodyear Ballpark
8. Peoria Sports Complex
9. Scottsdale Stadium
10. Sloan Park
11. Tempe Diablo Stadium
12. Hammond Stadium
13. Ed Smith Stadium
14. Camelback Ranch Glendale

BASEBALL SLANG (PAGE 11)

SOLUTIONS

WHO SAID IT? SPRING TRAINING EDITION (PAGE 13)

1. A
2. E
3. F
4. B
5. H
6. C
7. G
8. D

PLAYER POSITION IN NUMBERS (14)

1. H
2. D
3. E
4. C
5. A
6. F
7. I
8. B
9. G

BASEBALL MATHEMATICS (PAGE 14)

The baseball math shows a typical 4-6-3 double play. The second baseman (position 4) fields the ball and tosses it to the shortstop covering second (position 6). Then, the shortstop throws to first base (position 3) to get the second out. So, 4+6+3 = 2 outs!

BEST OPENING DAY MOMENTS (PAGE 16)

FIRST DAY JITTERS (PAGE 17)

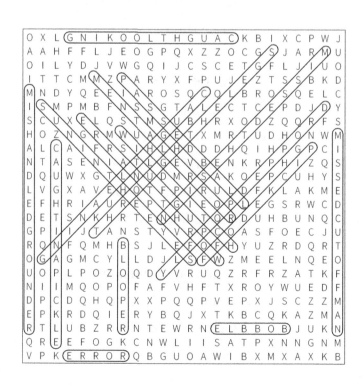

SOLUTIONS

WORLD SERIES REMATCH (PAGE 18)

2021 Atlanta Braves - Houston Astros
2015 Kansas City Royals - New York Mets
2009 New York Yankees - Philadelphia Phillies
2004 Boston Red Sox - St. Louis Cardinals
2001 Arizona Diamondbacks - New York Yankees
1997 Florida Marlins - Cleveland Indians
1996 New York Yankees - Atlanta Braves
1990 Cincinnati Reds - Oakland Athletics
1984 Detroit Tigers - San Diego Padres
1979 Pittsburgh Pirates - Baltimore Orioles
1974 Oakland Athletics - Los Angeles Dodgers
1965 Los Angeles Dodgers - Minnesota Twins
1958 New York Yankees - Milwaukee Braves
1953 New York Yankees - Brooklyn Dodgers
1948 Cleveland Indians - Boston Braves
1945 Detroit Tigers - Chicago Cubs
1944 St. Louis Cardinals - St. Louis Browns
1936 New York Yankees - New York Giants
1933 New York Giants - Washington Senators
1903 Boston Americans - Pittsburgh Pirates

OPENING DAY ABROAD (PAGE 19)

WHO SAID IT? OPENING DAY EDITION (PAGE 20)

1. A **2.** D **3.** B **4.** F **5.** C **6.** E **7.** H

FAMOUS IN THE BOOTH (PAGE 21)

1. Michael Kay **2.** Jerry Coleman
3. Jon Miller **4.** Jerry Remy
5. Joe Morgan **6.** John Sterling
7. Jack Buck **8.** Mel Allen
9. Russ Hodges **10.** Bob Costas
11. Harry Kalas **12.** Dick Enberg
13. Tim McCarver **14.** Dave Niehaus
15. Ernie Harwell **16.** Harry Caray
17. Phil Rizzuto **18.** Red Barber
19. Bob Uecker **20.** Vin Scully

OPENING DAY SECRET CRYPTOGRAM (PAGE 22)

Take me out to the ball game,
Take me out with the crowd;
Buy me some peanuts and Cracker Jack,
I don't care if I never get back.
Let me root, root, root for the home team,
If they don't win, it's a shame.
For it's one, two, three strikes, you're out,
at the old ball game.

ERNIE HARWELL OPENING DAY POEM (PAGE 23)

President, Scorecard, Wagner, Sandlot, Inches, Statistic, Democracy, Uniform, Rookie, Muscles, Ty Cobb, Bat, Religion, Stickball, Luckiest, Peanuts, Campanella, Boy

SOLUTIONS

PRESIDENTIAL FIRST PITCHES (PAGE 25)

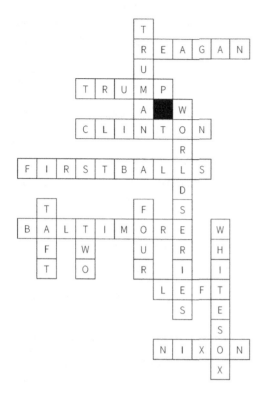

TEAM UNSCRAMBLE (PAGE 28)

1. Los Angeles Dodgers **2.** Tampa Bay Rays
3. Colorado Rockies **4.** Milwaukee Brewers
5. Washington Nationals **6.** Minnesota Twins
7. Arizona Diamondbacks **8.** Toronto Blue Jays
9. Baltimore Orioles **10.** New York Mets
11. Miami Marlins **12.** Seattle Mariners
13. Chicago Cubs **14.** San Diego Padres
15. Texas Rangers **16.** Baltimore Orioles

TEAMS & STADIUMS (PAGE 29)

1. Q **2.** F **3.** L **4.** T **5.** U **6.** H
7. X **8.** E **9.** R **10.** V **11.** Z **12.** M
13. Y **14.** O **15.** I **16.** J **17.** G **18.** S
19. B **20.** K **21.** D **22.** C **23.** P **24.** A
25. N **26.** W

PLAYER-MANAGERS (PAGE 26)

MLB TEAMS (PAGE 30)

SOLUTIONS

BALLPARKS ACROSS AMERICA (PAGE 31)

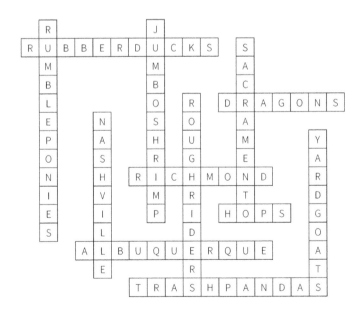

BALLPARK JUNK FOOD (PAGE 33)

THE WACKY AND WEIRD MINOR LEAGUES (PAGE 32)

BIZARRE FOOD BASEBALL EDITION (PAGE 34)

1. D **2.** K **3.** O **4.** E **5.** I **6.** J **7.** G **8.** A **9.** L **10.** F **11.** M **12.** B **13.** H **14.** C **15.** N

TEAMS AND DIVISIONS (PAGE 35)

AL East: New York Yankees, Tampa Bay Rays
AL Central: Cleveland Guardians,
Detroit Tigers, Minnesota Twins
AL West: Houston Astros, Seattle Mariners
NL East: Atlanta Braves, Miami Marlins
NL Central: Chicago Cubs, St. Louis Cardinals
NL West: Colorado Rockies, San Diego Padres,
San Francisco Giants

BALLPARK CONSTRUCTION TIMELINE (PAGE 36)

Group A: 10, 2, 14, 9, 5, 7, 1,
6, 15, 13, 3, 4, 12, 8, 11

Group B: 2, 14, 11, 4, 3, 7, 5,
10, 13, 12, 15, 8, 9, 1, 6

SOLUTIONS

TEAM NAME CHANGE (PAGE 37)

1. E
2. K
3. G
4. I
5. J
6. B
7. F
8. H
9. C
10. A
11. D

DEMOLISHED DIAMONDS (PAGE 38)

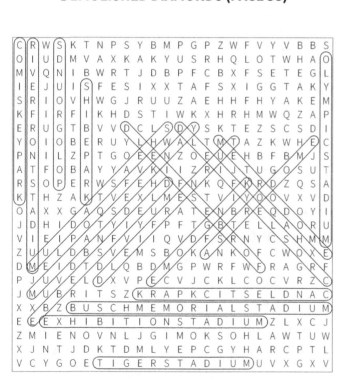

NEGRO LEAGUE TEAMS (PAGE 40)

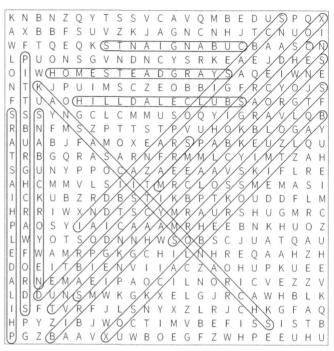

HISTORY OF JACKIE ROBINSON (PAGE 41)

WHO SAID IT? JACKIE ROBINSON EDITION (PAGE 42)

1. B 2. C 3. A 4. D 5. F 6. G 7. E

SOLUTIONS

BREAKING THE COLOR BARRIER (PAGE 43)

1. True

2. False

3. True

4. False

5. False

6. C **7.** D **8.** D **9.** B **10.** C

JACKIE ROBINSON TRIVIA (PAGE 44)

1. B **2.** C **3.** D **4.** A **5.** C **6.** D **7.** A **8.** B

STARS OF THE NEGRO LEAGUES (PAGE 45)

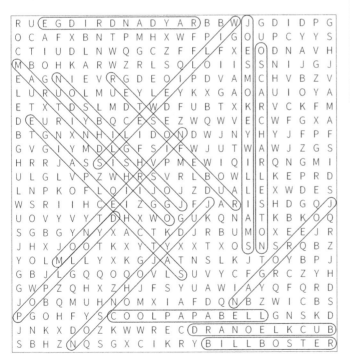

BASEBALL COLOR BARRIER TIMELINE (PAGE 46)

1947, 1994, 1920, 1955, 1975, 1959, 1971, 1939, 2020, 1997, 1945, 1947, 1987

NEGRO LEAGUES MYTHOLOGY (PAGE 47)

1. G **2.** D **3.** C **4.** A
5. E **6.** F **7.** B

WHO'S ON FIRST? (PAGE 49)

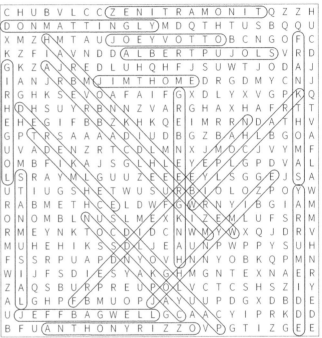

ALL-STAR SECOND BASEMEN (PAGE 50)

1. Nap Lajoie

2. Ryne Sandberg

3. Jackie Robinson

4. Chase Utley

5. Dustin Pedroia

6. Jeff Kent

7. Craig Biggio

8. Eddie Collins

9. Rogers Hornsby

10. Joe Morgan

11. Rod Carew

12. Jose Altuve

13. Bobby Grich

14. Charlie Gehringer

SOLUTIONS

NATIONAL & AMERICAN LEAGUE HISTORY (PAGE 51)

OUTFIELDERS FROM LEFT TO RIGHT (PAGE 53)

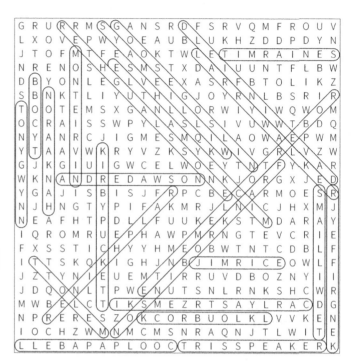

FIND THE COMMON THREAD (PAGE 52)

1. They all wear the number 27.

2. They all earned World Series MVP honors.

3. They all wear the number 22.

4. They all won the Home Run Derby.

5. They are all catchers.

6. They all play third base.

7. Their fathers all played in the Major Leagues.

8. They all play for the Seattle Mariners

9. They are all Cy Young winners.

10. They are all from Curaçao.

SHORTSTOPS ON TOP (PAGE 54)

1. Cal Ripken Jr
2. Omar Vizquel
3. Ozzie Smith
4. Ernie Banks
5. Pee Wee Reese
6. Troy Tulowitzski
7. Barry Larkin
8. Honus Wagner
9. Derek Jeter
10. Robin Yount
11. Luis Aparicio
12. Francisco Lindor
13. Lou Boudreau
14. Bo Bichette
15. Alan Trammell

SOLUTIONS

THE HOT CORNER (PAGE 55)

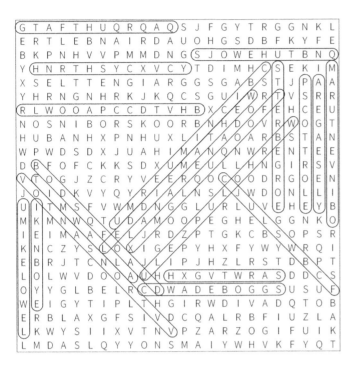

CY YOUNG STARS (PAGE 57)

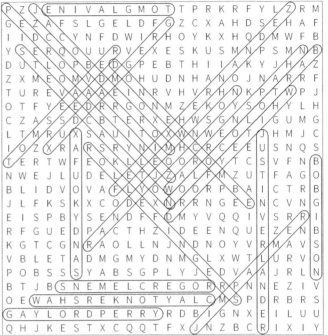

ALL-STAR GAME MOMENTS (PAGE 56)

GREATEST BEHIND THE PLATE (PAGE 58)

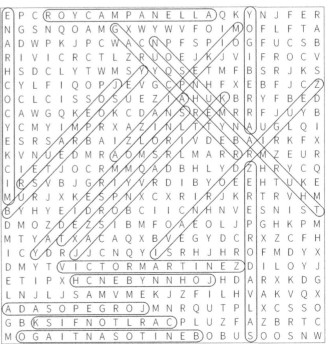

SOLUTIONS

BEST OF THE AL (PAGE 59)

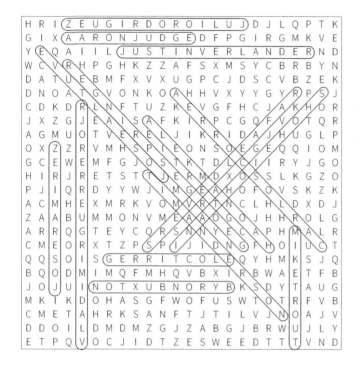

BEST OF THE NL (PAGE 60)

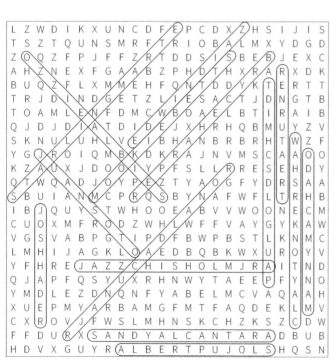

SERIOUS SLUGGERS (PAGE 62)

1. Ken Griffey Jr **2.** Barry Bonds

3. Vladimir Guerrero **4.** Albert Pujols

5. Sammy Sosa **6.** Mark McGwire

7. Babe Ruth **8.** Lou Gehrig

9. Harmon Killebrew **10.** Willie Mays

11. Jimmie Fox **12.** Hank Aaron

HOME RUN DERBY WINNERS (PAGE 63)

1. N **2.** A **3.** C **4.** H **5.** T **6.** B **7.** F **8.** D **9.** K

10. P **11.** Q **12.** V **13.** M **14.** U **15.** **16.** L

17. R **18.** E **19.** S **20.** J **21.** G **22.** O

MEMORABLE DERBY MOMENTS (PAGE 64)

SOLUTIONS

HITTING FOR AVERAGE (PAGE 65)

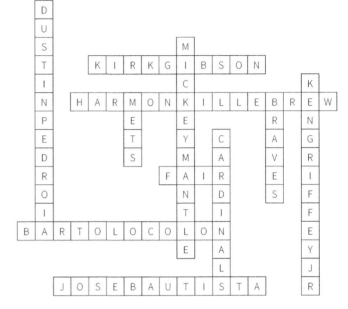

HOME RUN SWAGGER (PAGE 68)

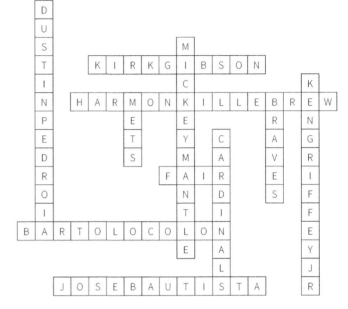

ACES WHO RAKE (PAGE 66)

1. Shohei Ohtani
2. Madison Bumgarner
3. Babe Ruth
4. Bob Gibson
5. Warren Spahn
6. Don Drysdale
7. Zack Greinke
8. Mike Hampton
9. Don Newcombe
10. Earl Wilson
11. Jim Kaat
12. Wes Ferrell

FAMOUS HOME RUN CALLS (PAGE 69)

1. A 2. C 3. B 4. D 5. F 6. E

TODAY'S BEST HOME RUN HITTERS (PAGE 70)

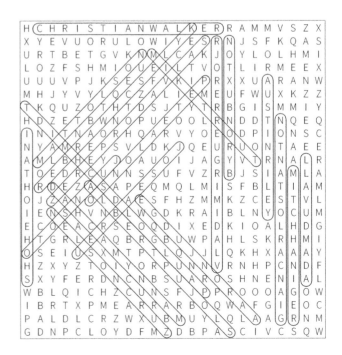

BEST HOME RUN HITTERS BY POSITION (PAGE 67)

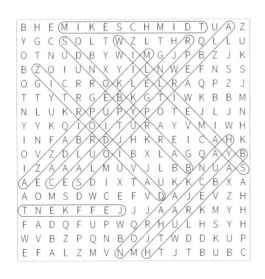

SOLUTIONS

FOUR FOUR-BAGGERS IN A GAME (PAGE 71)

THE 500 HOME RUN CLUB (PAGE 74)

1. Mark McGwire
2. Frank Robinson
3. Eddie Murray
4. Mel Ott
5. Willie McCovey
6. Harmon Killebrew
7. Reggie Jackson
8. Jimmie Foxx
9. Mike Schmidt
10. Miguel Cabrera
11. Frank Thomas
12. Gary Sheffield
13. Jim Thome
14. Rafael Palmeiro

15. Mickey Mantle
16. Sammy Sosa
17. Manny Ramirez
18. Ken Griffey Jr
19. Eddie Mathews
20. Ted Williams
21. David Ortiz
22. Ernie Banks
23. Willie Mays
24. Albert Pujols
25. Alex Rodriguez
26. Babe Ruth
27. Hank Aaron
28. Barry Bonds

MOST HOME RUNS IN A SEASON (PAGE 73)

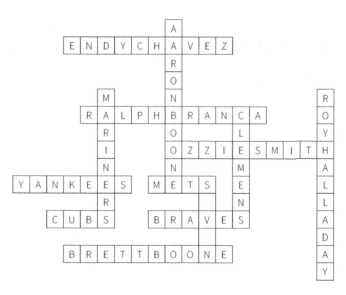

PLAYS FROM THE PLAYOFFS (PAGE 77)

SOLUTIONS

ALCS MVPS (PAGE 78)

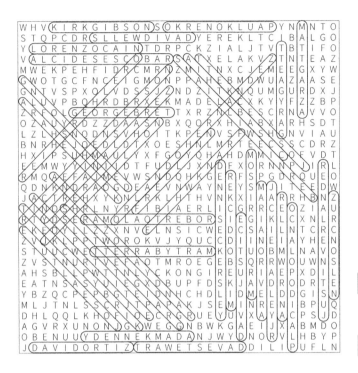

NLCS MVPS (PAGE 79)

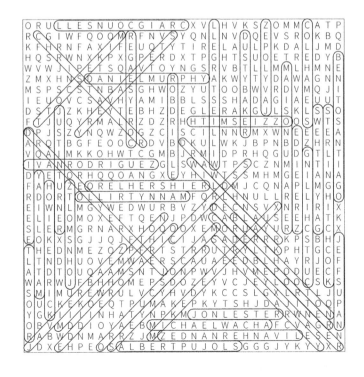

MUST-WIN PLAYOFF GAMES (PAGE 80)

WHO SAID IT? PLAYOFF EDITION (PAGE 81)

1. H **2.** D **3.** G **4.** B **5.** F **6.** C **7.** A **8.** E

POSTSEASON TRIVIA (PAGE 82)

1. True **2.** True
3. False **4.** True
5. False **6.** True

7. B
8. D
9. A
10. D
11. C
12. B

SOLUTIONS

TOP PLAYOFF PITCHING PERFORMANCES (PAGE 83)

POSTSEASON UPSETS (PAGE 85)

PLAYOFF RIVALRIES (PAGE 86)

1. H **2.** F **3.** A **4.** J **5.** I **6.** B **7.** D **8.** K
9. C **10.** M **11.** E **12.** G **13.** L

POSTSEASON BUZZWORDS (PAGE 84)

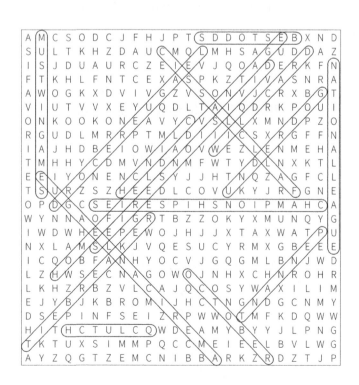

WORLD SERIES REMATCH (PAGE 88)

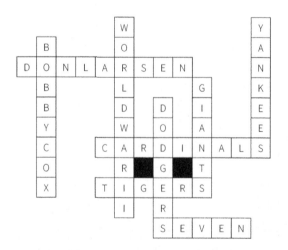

MOST FRANCHISE WORLD SERIES TITLES (PAGE 89)

1. F **2.** E **3.** G **4.** D **5.** B **6.** C **7.** A

SOLUTIONS

WORLD SERIES GLORY (PAGE 90)

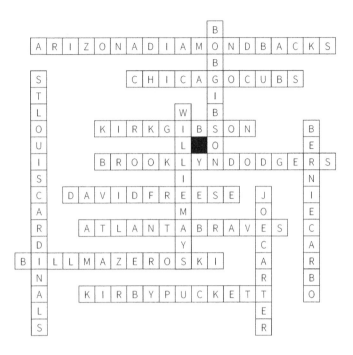

WORLD SERIES HISTORY (PAGE 93)

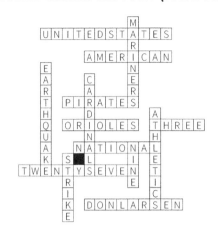

BAD TIMING BLUNDERS (PAGE 94)

WHO SAID IT? WORLD SERIES EDITION (PAGE 91)

1. C **2.** A **3.** G **4.** I **5.** D
6. F **7.** E **8.** B **9.** H

WORLD SERIES DROUGHTS (PAGE 92)

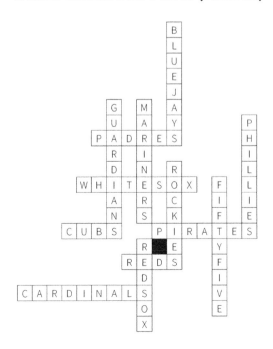

WORLD SERIES MVPS (2000 - PRESENT) (PAGE 95)

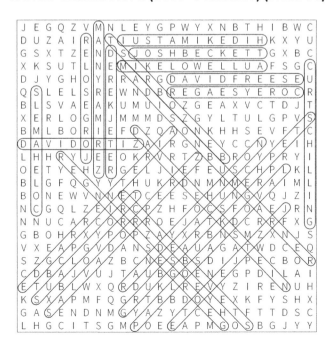

SOLUTIONS

WORLD SERIES MVPS 1980 - 1999 (PAGE 96)

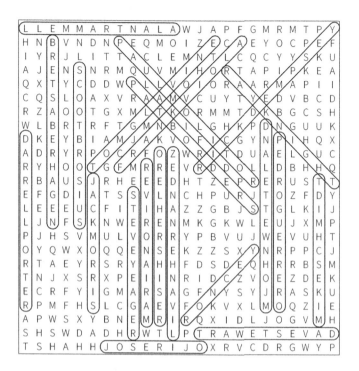

FUTURE HALL OF FAMERS (PAGE 100)

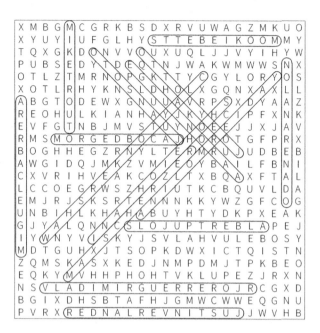

HALL OF FAME NICKNAMES (PAGE 101)

1. S **2.** A **3.** O **4.** F **5.** I **6.** N **7.** G **8.** R **9.** J **10.** M
11. B **12.** P **13.** D **14.** E **15.** K **16.** Q **17.** C **18.** T
19. H **20.** L

MYSTERY WORLD SERIES CRYPTOGRAM (PAGE 96)

The Commissioner's Trophy

MATCH THE CAREER RECORD TO THE PLAYER (PAGE 98)

1. A **2.** G **3.** O **4.** B **5.** J **6.** M **7.** F **8.** D **9.** P
10. E/N **11.** E/N **12.** K/L **13.** C **14.** K/L **15.** H **16.** I

HALL OF FAME MANAGERS (PAGE 102)

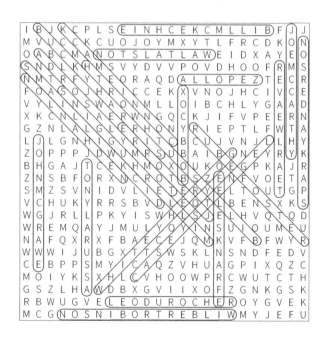

NAME THE HALL OF FAME PLAYER (PAGE 99)

1. Ken Griffey Jr **2.** Tim Raines **3.** Sandy Koufax
4. Roger Maris **5.** Satchel Paige **6.** Jackie Robinson
7. Derek Jeter **8.** Ty Cobb

SOLUTIONS

HITTERS WITH 3,000 HITS (PAGE 103)

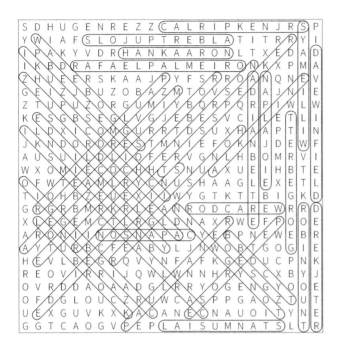

PITCHERS WITH 300 WINS (PAGE 104)

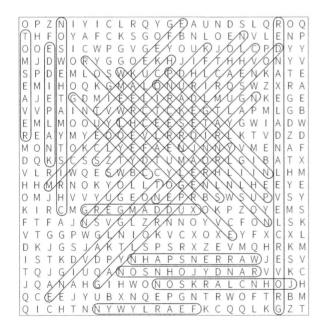

LOU GEHRIG FAREWELL SPEECH FILL IN THE BLANKS (PAGE 105)

Weeks, Luckiest, Earth, Seventeen, Grand, Honor, Empire, Manager, Giants, Gift, Groundskeepers, Daughter, Education, Wife, Courage, Tough

FIND THE COMMON THREAD (PAGE 106)

1. They all share the nickname "The Kid."

2. They all wore the number **5** on their uniforms.

3. They all played catcher.

4. They are all part of a father-son MLB duo.

5. All were members of the 2001 Diamondbacks World Series team.

6. They were all born in Illinois.

7. They all won the Cy Young Award.

8. They all earned World Series MVP honors.

9. They were all banned from baseball at some point (Mantle and Mays were reinstated later).

10. They are all shortstops in the Hall of Fame.

FAMOUS IN THE BOOTH (PAGE 107)

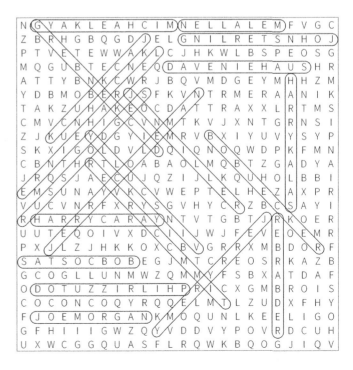

SOLUTIONS

FAVORITE BASEBALL MOVIES (PAGE 109)

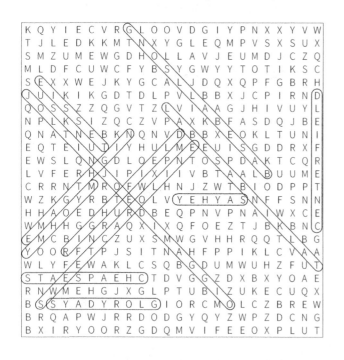

BASEBALL IN MUSIC (PAGE 110)

BASEBALL TRADES THAT ACTUALLY HAPPENED (PAGE 112)

1. A **2.** C **3.** D **4.** B **5.** B **6.** A

KICKED OUT OF BASEBALL (PAGE 113)

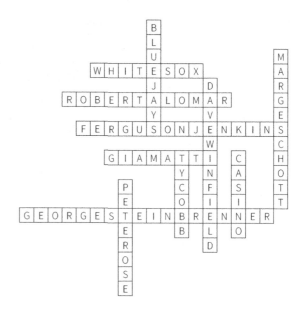

YOGI-ISMS FILL IN THE BLANKS (PAGE 114)

Over, Think, Liars, Funerals, Love, Perfect, Mental, Five, Nothing, Déjà Vu, Nickel, Fork, Amphibious, Future, Observe

CELEBRITY BASEBALL FANS (PAGE 115)

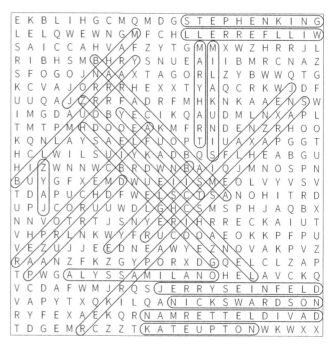

SOLUTIONS

BASEBALL MEMORABILIA YOU WISH YOU HAD (PAGE 116)

MULTI-SPORT PLAYERS (PAGE 118)

AWARDS, TROPHIES, AND ACCOLADES (PAGE 117)

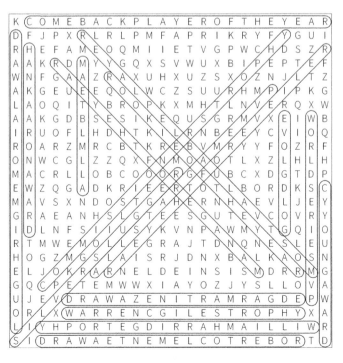

WEIRD BASEBALL NAMES (PAGE 119)